PERSPECTIVES IN NC ... RITY

MATHEMATICS LECTURE NOTE SERIES

E. Artin and J. Tate *Harvard University*	CLASS FIELD THEORY
Michael Atiyah *Oxford University*	K-THEORY
Hyman Bass *Columbia University*	ALGEBRAIC K-THEORY
Raoul Bott *Harvard University*	LECTURES ON K(X)
Paul J. Cohen *Stanford University*	SET THEORY AND THE CONTINUUM HYPOTHESIS
Walter Feit *Yale University*	CHARACTERS OF FINITE GROUPS
Marvin J. Greenberg *Northeastern University*	LECTURES ON ALGEBRAIC TOPOLOGY
Robin Hartshorne *Harvard University*	FOUNDATIONS OF PROJECTIVE GEOMETRY
Irving Kaplansky *University of Chicago*	RINGS OF OPERATORS
Serge Lang *Columbia University*	ALGEBRAIC FUNCTIONS
Serge Lang *Columbia University*	RAPPORT SUR LA COHOMOLOGIE DES GROUPES
I. G. Macdonald *Oxford University*	ALGEBRAIC GEOMETRY: INTRODUCTION TO SCHEMES
George Mackey *Harvard University*	INDUCED REPRESENTATIONS OF GROUPS AND QUANTUM MECHANICS
Richard Palais *Brandeis University*	FOUNDATIONS OF GLOBAL NON-LINEAR ANALYSIS
D. S. Passman *Yale University*	PERMUTATION GROUPS
Jean-Pierre Serre *Collège de France*	ABELIAN *l*-ADIC REPRESENTATIONS AND ELLIPTIC CURVES
Jean-Pierre Serre *Collège de France*	ALGEBRES DE LIE SEMI-SIMPLES COMPLEXES
Jean-Pierre Serre *Collège de France*	LIE ALGEBRAS AND LIE GROUPS

PERSPECTIVES IN NONLINEARITY

An Introduction to Nonlinear Analysis

MELVYN BERGER and MARION BERGER

University of Minnesota

W. A. BENJAMIN, INC.

New York 1968 Amsterdam

PERSPECTIVES IN NONLINEARITY An Introduction to Nonlinear Analysis

Library of Congress Catalog Card Number 68-58448
Manufactured in the United States of America
12345M321098

The manuscript was put into production on September 18, 1968; this volume was published on December 3, 1968

W. A. BENJAMIN, INC.
New York, New York 10016

A Note from the Publisher

This volume was printed directly from a typescript prepared by the author, who takes full responsibility for its content and appearance. The Publisher has not performed his usual functions of reviewing, editing, typesetting, and proofreading the material prior to publication.

The Publisher fully endorses this informal and quick method of publishing lecture notes at a moderate price, and he wishes to thank the author for preparing the material for publication.

CONTENTS

'ace 1

pter 1. Once Over Lightly 3

1-1. Diophantine Equations and the Genus of an Algebraic Plane Curve 4
1-2. Zeros and Critical Points of Analytic Functions of One Complex Variable 13
1-3. Some General Problems of Nonlinear Analysis 20
1-4. Applications of Nonlinear Problems 25

pter 2. Finite Dimensional Systems in $\mathbb{R}^n$ 31

2-1. The Definition of Degree of a Mapping 32
2-2. Some Properties of the Degree of a Mapping 45
2-3. Gradient Systems and Their Basic Properties 56
2-4. Gradient Systems with Nondegenerate Critical Points 64
2-5. Critical Points for General Gradient Systems 77
2-6. Systems Deformable to Gradient Systems 87

pter 3. Infinite Dimensional Systems 93

3-1. The Degree of a Class of Operators in Spaces of Infinite Dimension 95
3-2. A Special Class of Noncompact Operators 105
3-3. Gradient Operators and Their Properties 107
3-4. A Remark on the Theory of Critical Points of Infinite Dimensional Gradient Operators 117
3-5. Local Behavior of Nonlinear Operator Equations in Hilbert Space 118

ter 4. Applications 133

4-1. Global Univalence 133
4-2. Topics in Nonlinear Autonomous Ordinary Differential Equations 142
4-3. Topics in Elliptic Partial Differential Equations 159

ndix I. The Axioms of Homology Theory 183

ndix II. Standard Results from Analysis 186

PREFACE

These notes are based on lectures given at the University of Minnesota and the Courant Institute of Mathematical Sciences, New York University, in 1966 and 1967. Our aim has been to present some qualitative aspects of nonlinear analysis, which we think are important, in as simple and direct a manner as possible. Thus we have neither striven for results of the utmost generality nor complicated the text by introducing an excess number of new concepts. In this way we hope to make the ideas presented accessible to persons who enjoy mathematics and its applications but are not specialists in nonlinear analysis. To accomplish this goal in a small book we have had to sketch the ideas of a few proofs and to specialize the general theory of nonlinear analysis on finite and infinite dimensional differentiable manifolds. The interested reader will find this theory discussed in the monographs, Lectures on Nonlinear Functional Analysis by J. T. Schwartz, and Foundations of Global Nonlinear Analysis by R. S. Palais. Furthermore, our choice of material was necessarily selective, for example, iterative results such as Newton's method and Nash's implicit function theorem have been omitted. Nonetheless we believe that the material discussed here has sufficient beauty to induce the reader to further excursions into nonlinear analysis.

Our text is divided into four chapters and two appendices. Chapter 1 is intended to be a partial answer to the question: What are some of the problems of nonlinear analysis and how have they been studied in previous generations? Chapter 2 introduces the concepts of the degree of a continuous mapping, and the theory of critical points of real-valued functions in finite dimensional Euclidean spaces $\mathbb{R}^n$. In Chapter 3 we show how the ideas of Chapter 2 can be carried over to infinite dimensional spaces. Appendices 1 and 2 at the end of the book include some preliminary material necessary to the understanding of Chapters 2 and 3. In Chapter 4 we select a few specific nonlinear problems and indicate just how the methods of the previous chapters can be used to study these problems. The first-mentioned problem in Chapter 4, global univalence, is of great interest outside of mathematics (for example, to mathematical economists in the study of international trade and to applied mathematicians studying elastic deformations). Similarly the topics of differential equations (ordinary and partial) discussed in

Chapter 4 are basic to the understanding of many physical processes of nature.

We are grateful to the Courant Institute and Brooklyn College of CUNY for giving us the opportunity to begin work on this monograph. We would also like to thank the people who helped in the preparation of this manuscript especially Professors L. Bers and W. Littman.

Minneapolis, Minnesota
September, 1968

M.S.B.
M.S.B.

CHAPTER 1

ONCE OVER LIGHTLY

The theory of linear equations in a finite number of real variables can be studied by introducing such notions as matrix, rank of a matrix and determinant. In this book we shall consider the possibility of extending these notions to equations that are not necessarily linear and which involve possibly infinitely many unknowns. The unifying principle in our study can be simply expressed. For specific types of equations we shall attempt to discover systems of "invariants" that can be used to classify equations of a given type and to express properties of the real solutions of these equations. This viewpoint will open a broad and unified vista on a large number of diverse mathematical problems, as well as sufficient depth of treatment to prove many striking results. In this chapter we illustrate this approach by considering the solvability of equations in integers and of systems of equations defined by the real and imaginary parts of an analytic function of a complex variable. The ideas that arise in these examples will recur throughout our study.

§1-1. DIOPHANTINE EQUATIONS AND THE GENUS OF AN ALGEBRAIC PLANE CURVE

One of the earliest studies of nonlinear equations was made by the Greek Diophantus over 2000 years ago. In the footsteps of this early study, we consider the following "diophantine" problem:

> *Find all the integers which satisfy the equation $f(x_1,x_2,x_3) = 0$ where $f(x_1,x_2,x_3)$ is some homogeneous polynomial of degree n in x_1, x_2, x_3 with integer coefficients.* (P_1)

For example, finding the integer solutions of $x_1^2 + x_2^2 = x_3^2$ has been of interest since Pythagoras and is relatively simple to solve. While the problem of finding integral solutions of $x_1^n + x_2^n = x_3^n$ for general $n > 2$, known as "Fermat's Last Problem", has resisted the efforts of many men of renown. Thus a complete answer to the diophantine problem (P_1) still is an impossible task. However we shall present a "modern" approach to (P_1) which at least gives some insight into the general problem. We classify all homogeneous polynomials $f(x_1,x_2,x_3)$ by a nonnegative integer p and solve if $p = 0$. This integer p serves as a measure of the difficulty of the associated diophantine problem. In the case $p = 0$, the integral solutions of $f(x_1,x_2,x_3) = 0$ will always be countably infinite in number provided the degree of the polynomial f is odd.

The underlying idea is to consider the equation $f(x_1,x_2,x_3) = 0$ as the locus of a curve Γ in the complex projective plane X, that is the space consisting of all points $x = (x_1,x_2,x_3)$ where x_1, x_2, x_3 are complex numbers and the points x and $y = (y_1,y_2,y_3)$ are equivalent if x_i and y_i are proportional. (Note: the point (0,0,0), having no geometric meaning in the projective plane, is always excluded from consideration.) Such curves are then associated with a certain integer p, called the genus of Γ. The integer p is just the sort of invariant we are seeking. Indeed if $p = 0$, Γ is called "rational" and it can be shown that Γ can be given parametrically by $x_1 = x_1(t)$, $x_2 = x_2(t)$, $x_3 = x_3(t)$, where the $x_i(t)$ are polynomials in t. (Furthermore, if $p \neq 0$ such a parametrization is impossible.) If these polynomials have rational coefficients, our diophantine problem can be completely solved. For then all integer solutions of $f(x_1,x_2,x_3) = 0$ can be found by letting the parameter t vary in such a way that $x_1(t)$, $x_2(t)$, $x_3(t)$ are always integers. An interesting fact is that one can tell whether a curve Γ is rational without explicitly finding any parametrization. Indeed we now present a reasonably simple algorithm for computing the genus of Γ. When carried through with sufficient patience an elaborated version of this algorithm also provides a parametrization of Γ, provided of course that $p = 0$.

First we impose certain simplifying assumptions on f. It is important here to note that the structural properties of Γ in our study will be completely determined by the <u>singular points</u> of f, or equivalently of Γ, that is points x at which $f_{x_1} = f_{x_2} = f_{x_3} = 0$, where f_{x_1}, f_{x_2}, and f_{x_3} indicate the partial derivatives of f with respect to x_1, x_2, x_3. We assume first, without loss of generality, that f is an irreducible polynomial of degree n over the complex numbers, that is $f(x_1,x_2,x_3)$ is not the product of two homogeneous polynomials in x_1, x_2, x_3. Secondly we assume that the singular points of Γ have multiplicity 2, that is, although all first order derivatives of $f(x_1,x_2,x_3)$ vanish at the singular point some second order derivative does not vanish. (This assumption eliminates the consideration of curves with singular points of multiplicity $k > 2$ at which all derivatives of f up to and including order $(k - 1)$

vanish, but some k-th derivative does not vanish. Such singular points (are degenerate and) can be "resolved" into an equivalent number of (nondegenerate) singular points of multiplicity 2. This degeneracy is an inevitable feature of nonlinear problems and will be mentioned in other contexts throughout the sequel.)

Figure 1. Curves with singular points P, P' of multiplicities respectively 2 and greater than 2.

With these preliminaries we can now compute the genus as follows.

DEFINITION 1-1. *The genus of an algebraic curve* Γ *defined by* $f(x_1,x_2,x_3) = 0$ *and satisfying the above assumptions is the integer* $p = (1/2)(n-1)(n-2) - N$, *where* n *is the degree of* f *and* N *is the number of singular points of* Γ. *If* $p = 0$, *we call* Γ *a rational curve*.

THEOREM 1-2. *The maximum number of singular points for an irreducible curve* Γ_n *of degree* n *is* $(1/2)(n-1)(n-2)$. *Thus* $p \geq 0$, *and* $p = 0$ *if* Γ_n *has exactly the maximum number* $(1/2)(n - 1)(n - 2)$ *of singular points*.

Proof. The result for $n = 1$ takes no thought, for then Γ is a straight line. For $n = 2$ (that is, for conics) see Example 1-2 and Exercise 1-2 below. For $n > 2$, the proof is somewhat more difficult and will be sketched below. Our argument is based on two lemmas.

LEMMA 1-3. (Bezout) *Let* $g(x_1,x_2,x_3) = 0$ *and* $h(x_1,x_2,x_3) = 0$ *be homogeneous polynomial equations of degree* p *and* q *respectively, with no common factor of degree* > 0. *Then there exist exactly* pq *solutions of this system*. (*Note that if a solution* $(\bar{x}_1,\bar{x}_2,\bar{x}_3)$ *is a singular point of multiplicity* j *for* $g(x_1,x_2,x_3) = 0$ *and* k *for* $h(x_1,x_2,x_3) = 0$, $(\bar{x}_1,\bar{x}_2,\bar{x}_3)$ *is counted here as* jk *distinct solutions*.)

Proof. This is a standard algebraic result whose proof appears in numerous texts [for example, R. J. Walker [1] p. 111] and hence will not appear here.

LEMMA 1-4. *The set of homogeneous polynomials of degree* n *in the space* X *can be considered as a linear space of dimension* $(1/2)n(n + 3)$.

Proof. A polynomial $f(x_1,x_2,x_3) = \Sigma\, a_{ijk}x_1{}^i x_2{}^j x_3{}^k$, where

$i, j, k \geq 0$ and $i + j + k = n$, is uniquely determined by its coefficients to within a constant factor. To count the number M of these coefficients we consider $f(x_1, x_2, 1)$ and let the number of terms of degree i of the form $x_1^j x_2^{i-j}$ be n_i. Thus $M = \Sigma_{i=0}^n n_i = \Sigma_{i=0}^n (i + 1) = (1/2)(n + 1)(n + 2)$. Hence the set $\{a_{ijk}\}$ can be considered as coordinates for Γ_n in a linear space of dimension $M - 1 = (1/2)n(n + 3)$. ||

<u>Proof of Theorem</u> 1-2 <u>for</u> $n > 2$. We obtain a contradiction by supposing that Γ_n has $(1/2)(n - 1)(n - 2) + 1$ singular points. Consider the linear space of curves of degree $(n - 2)$ through these points. As the requirement that a curve Γ pass through a given point imposes one linear condition on the coefficients of Γ, the dimension of the space of curves is, by Lemma 1-4, $(1/2)(n - 2)(n + 1) - [(1/2)(n - 1)(n - 2) + 1] = n - 3$. Thus a member of this family, Γ_{n-2}, can be made to pass through $(n - 3)$ other points of Γ_n. To get a contradiction, we count the number of points in the intersection $\Gamma_n \cap \Gamma_{n-2}$ according to multiplicity. This number is at least $2[(1/2)(n - 1)(n - 2) + 1] + (n - 3) = n(n - 2) + 1$. But this contradicts Bezout's Lemma, as Γ_n has degree n, Γ_{n-2} degree $n - 2$, and Γ_n is irreducible. ||

The method of proof above yields a construction for the parametrization of a rational curve Γ_n. First consider the case of a rational cubic curve Γ_3. By definition, such a curve has exactly one singular point, and by Bezout's Lemma, an arbitrary line through this point whose equation contains a parameter t intersects the curve in one other point. As the parameter t varies, this point of intersection traces out Γ_3, and so the coordinates of the point can be given by polynomials in t. Thus we have the required parametrization.

EXAMPLE 1-1. <u>Integer solutions of</u> $f(x_1,x_2,x_3) = x_1{}^3 + x_2{}^3 - x_1x_2x_3 = 0$. Except for the excluded point (0,0,0), the only singular point is (0,0,1). As $f_{x_1x_2} = -x_3 \neq 0$ at (0,0,1), this point has multiplicity 2. Thus by Theorem 1-2 the associated curve Γ_3 is rational as $p = (1/2)(3 - 1)(3 - 2) - 1 = 0$. Now following the proof of the theorem, we consider the lines $x_2 = tx_1$ through (0,0,1). Upon solving the equations $f(x_1,x_2,x_3) = 0$ and $x_2 = tx_1$ we obtain as points of intersection the one parameter family $(t,t^2,1 + t^3)$. As the parameter t runs through all complex numbers, we obtain all points on Γ_3. Hence all integer solutions of the equation can be found by letting the parameter run through all integer values. There are hence a countably infinite number of solutions.

The next case is a rational curve Γ_4 of degree 4. By definition, Γ_4 has exactly 3 singular points each of multiplicity 2. As in the proof of Theorem 1-2, we consider the curves of degree $4 - 2 = 2$ through these singular points and through another fixed point which may be chosen so as to minimize the computations involved. The dimension of this family of curves is $(1/2)(4 - 2)(4 + 1) - (1/2)(4 - 1)(4 - 2) - 1 = 1$ and so its equation can be expressed in terms of a parameter t. The curves Γ_4 and $\Gamma_2(t)$ intersect in $(4 - 1)(4 - 2) + (4 - 3) = 7$ known points, and thus by Bezout's Lemma in another point, whose coordinates may be expressed in terms of t. This construction yields a parametrization of Γ_4 which may be readily generalized to rational curves of degree n.

EXAMPLE 1-2. The rational points on irreducible plane conics $F(x_1,x_2) = ax_1^2 + 2bx_1x_2 + cx_2^2 + dx_1 + ex_2 + f = 0$ with rational coefficients. Such problems can be reduced to problems of parametrization as all such conics are "rational". Indeed to every solution of $F(x_1,x_2) = 0$ in rational numbers, corresponds a solution of the associated homogeneous polynomial equation $x_3^2F(x_1/x_3,x_2/x_3) = 0$ with $x_3 \neq 0$. Next observe that the existence of one rational point on such a conic guarantees the existence of a countably infinite number of such points. For if α and β are rational numbers with

$F(\alpha,\beta) = 0$, a short computation shows that a line through (α,β) with rational slope t cuts $F(x_1,x_2) = 0$ again at a point with coordinates $x_i = (a_i + b_i t + c_i t^2)/(a + bt + ct^2)$, $(i = 1,2)$, where a_i, b_i, c_i are polynomials in α, β, a, b, c, d, e, f. (See Exercises.) Now, an irreducible conic is a hyperbola, ellipse, or parabola. A parabola always has rational points; for any parabola may be transformed by linear transformations with rational coefficients into the form $x_1 = x_2^2$. On the other hand, ellipses and hyperbolas may have no rational points. For example, $x_1^2 + x_2^2 = 3x_3^2$ has no solutions in integers (excluding $(0,0,0)$). For if $(\bar{x}_1,\bar{x}_2,\bar{x}_3)$ were the smallest positive solution of $x_1^2 + x_2^2 = 3x_3^2$, then modulo 3 both $\bar{x}_1$ and $\bar{x}_2$ would be congruent to 0 (since squares can only be congruent to 0 or 1 modulo 3). Hence $\bar{x}_1$, $\bar{x}_2$, and (from the equation) $\bar{x}_3$ must all be divisible by 3; a contradiction.

The above examples illustrate an interesting distinction among rational curves with integer coefficients. Namely the associated equations of odd degree always have a countably infinite number of solutions in integers, while equations of even degree may have no such solutions. For a proof we refer to the book of Skolem [2] Chapter 5. This fact was mentioned by Hilbert and Hurwitz in 1891 and by Poincaré in 1901 in his famous paper "Sur les proprietés arithmetiques des courbes algebriques" where the problem for curves with genus ≥ 1 is also considered.

Exercises

1-1. Prove that every singular point of $f(x_1,x_2,x_3)$ lies on the curve Γ defined by $f(x_1,x_2,x_3) = 0$.

1-2. Prove that (i) the conic $\Sigma_{i,j=1,2,3}\, a_{ij}x_ix_j$ is reducible if and only if $\det|a_{ij}| = 0$,

and (ii) a conic is rational, by showing that an irreducible conic has no singular point other than $(0,0,0)$.

1-3. Obtain the parametrization of the conic $x_3^2F(x_1/x_3,x_2/x_3) = 0$ with rational point $(\alpha,\beta,1)$ mentioned in Example 1-2.

1-4. (On Fermat's Last Theorem). Compute the genus of the curve $x_1^n + x_2^n = x_3^n$ where n is an integer. Compute all solutions in integers for $n = 2$, and show there are no solutions with $x_1x_2x_3 \neq 0$ for $n = 3$. (See Nagell [3]).

1-5. Compute the genus of the following algebraic curves and find all integer solutions of the associated equations

(a) $x_1x_2x_3 = x_1^3 + x_1^2x_2 + x_1x_2^2 + 2x_2^3$

(b) $x_1^4 + x_1^2x_2^2 - x_3^2x_2^2 - 2x_3^2x_1^2 + x_3^4 = 0.$

§1-2. ZEROS AND CRITICAL POINTS OF ANALYTIC FUNCTIONS OF ONE COMPLEX VARIABLE

The next step in our study of solutions of nonlinear

equations $f = 0$ is to consider functions f which can be regarded as infinite sums of polynomials. To this end, let $x, y \in \mathbb{R}$ and $z = x + iy$. Suppose $f(z) = u(x,y) + iv(x,y) = |f(z)| \exp[i(\arg f(z))]$ is a single-valued analytic function in a bounded simply connected domain D of the complex plane. Then the zeros of $f(z)$ can be considered from any of the following points of view:

(i) the real solutions of the two equations $u(x,y) = 0$ and $v(x,y) = 0$. Furthermore the principle of the argument can be employed in the determination of the location of these zeros. More particularly, if C is a simple closed rectifiable curve in D on which $f(z)$ does not vanish, then the number η of zeros of f inside C can be calculated entirely from the action of f on C by the formula

$$\eta = \frac{1}{2\pi i} \int_C \frac{f'(z)}{f(z)}\, dz = \frac{1}{2\pi i} \int_C d(\log f(z)) = \frac{1}{2\pi} \int_C d(\arg f(z))$$

(ii) the critical points of some analytic function $g(z)$ that is points where $g'(z) = 0$. Indeed every analytic function $f(z)$ defined on a simply connected domain can be regarded as the derivative of some analytic function $g(z)$. Furthermore, if $g(z) = U(x,y) + iV(x,y)$ the Cauchy-Riemann equations for $g(z)$ namely, $U_x = V_y$, $U_y = -V_x$, guarantee that the critical points of $g(z)$ can be found by studying the critical points of the real-valued function U, that is points (x,y) where $U_x = U_y = 0$.

(iii) points mapped into the point $(0,0)$ by the mapping of the plane into itself defined by the formula $(x,y) \to (u(x,y),v(x,y))$.

In subsequent work each of these approaches to the study of zeros of systems of equations will be generalized. For example, the principle of the argument for analytic functions can be extended to count the zeros of large classes of general systems of equations in finite and even infinitely many variables. To see this fact more clearly for functions of two variables, we reexamine the viewpoint (i) above. Consider any simple closed curve C and two continuous functions $u(x,y)$ and $v(x,y)$ which do not necessarily comprise the real and imaginary parts of an analytic function. Assume that u and v do not vanish simultaneously on C. Denoting by θ, $\arctan(v/u)$, we obtain the following expression for the angle of rotation θ_C of the vector (u,v) on one turn of the circumference C:

$$\theta_C = \int_C d\theta = \int_C d[\arctan(v/u)] = \int_C \frac{u\,dv - v\,du}{u^2 + v^2} \qquad (1\text{-}1)$$

This formula represents a generalization of the principle of the argument. The number $\theta_C/2\pi = I$ turns out to be an integer; positive, negative, or zero. If there is exactly one zero (a,b) of $u(x,y)$ and $v(x,y)$ in C, this integer I is called the index of the point (a,b) with respect to the system (u,v). Since the zeros of an analytic function are isolated, the index of any zero of such a function is defined, and the principle of the argument insures that this number is always a positive integer. In Chapter 2 we shall investigate the following properties and their n-dimensional analogues.

(i) the index is independent of the particular simple closed curve C enclosing only the zero at (a,b).

(ii) $\theta_C = 0$ if u and v have no common zero in C.

(iii) if u and v have a finite number k of zeros in C (counted according to multiplicity) with associated indices $I_1, I_2, \ldots, I_k$ then $\theta_C = 2\pi \Sigma_{j=1}^{k} I_j$.

Thus we have the following principle for finding zeros: If $\theta_C \neq 0$, the system (u,v) must have a zero in C. (The generalization of this result, to be mentioned later, is called the Leray-Schauder Fixed Point Theorem.)

We also reexamine the second aspect of the zeros of an analytic function. First recall the fact that the real and imaginary parts of an analytic function in D are harmonic functions, that is, they satisfy the equation $u_{xx} + u_{yy} = 0$ in D, and we can thus state facts concerning the zeros of analytic functions in terms of real-valued harmonic functions. Now, a general real-valued function of two variables $g(x,y)$ can have any of three types of nondegenerate critical points. (that is, points with $\text{grad } g = 0$ but $g_{xx}g_{yy} - g_{xy}^2 \neq 0$), relative minima or saddle points. In D however, a nonconstant harmonic function can only have saddle points. The reason for this fact is the maximum principle for harmonic functions which states that a nonconstant harmonic function cannot achieve its maximum or minimum in the interior of D. Since the zeros of an analytic function are isolated, the critical points of a nonconstant harmonic function are isolated too. Hence the index of a zero of the gradient of a harmonic function is defined, and is always a negative integer (see Exercise 1-7).

EXAMPLE 1-3. <u>The index of an isolated relative maximum or minimum</u> (x_0,y_0) <u>of the gradient of a continuously differentiable function</u> $f(x,y)$ <u>is one</u>. (Instead of using the formula (1-1) we prefer a more geometric argument.) Suppose, for example, (x_0,y_0) is a relative minimum and an isolated critical point of $f(x,y)$. Then for sufficiently small $\epsilon > 0$ and for (x,y) in a neighborhood of (x_0,y_0) the level surface $C = \{(x,y) | f(x,y) = f(x_0,y_0) + \epsilon\}$ is a closed bounded curve with continuously varying tangent enclosing the single critical point (x_0,y_0). (Note: grad $f \neq 0$ on C implies C has no self-intersections.) On C, as $df = 0$ we have $f_x\, dx + f_y\, dy = 0$. Thus the gradient vector (f_x,f_y) is perpendicular to the tangent vector (dx,dy) at all points of C and thus continuously varies along either the outward or inward normal to C. (See Fig. 2.) But in one (positively-oriented) rotation of C, the normal to C changes by exactly $+2\pi$ radians. Thus the index under consideration is one. (A similar argument holds for a relative maximum. It will be shown later that the index of a saddle point is negative.)

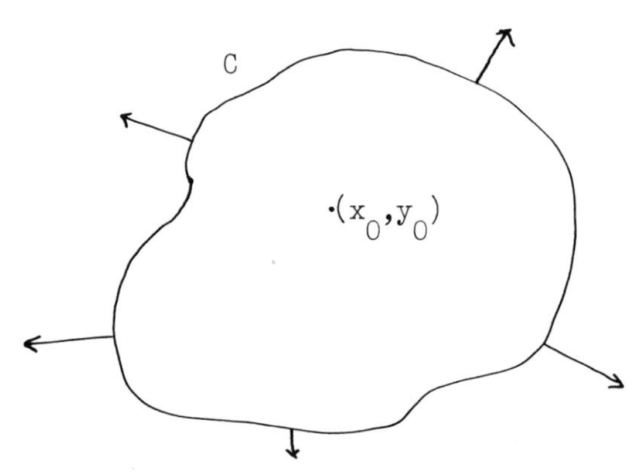

Figure 2. The index of grad f at an isolated relative maximum or minimum (x_0,y_0) is one.

We wish to mention two other facts concerning the stability of zeros of an analytic function that have interesting consequences in later work. First Rouché's Theorem; i.e. if $f(z)$ does not vanish on C, then the number of zeros of f

in C does not change when $f(z)$ is slightly perturbed to $f(z) + g(z)$ provided $|g(z)|$ is sufficiently small relative to f, and g is analytic in and on C. Secondly, a result of Hurwitz; that if $f(z) \neq 0$ in C, the number of zeros of f in C is a continuous function of f with respect to uniform convergence, that is, if $f_n(z)$ is a sequence of analytic functions with $f_n(z) \to f(z)$ uniformly in C, then $\eta_{f_n(z)} \to \eta_{f(z)}$. For general systems of functions these ideas extend to show, roughly speaking, that the invariant associated with the number of zeros in a region D can be calculated by approximation once its value is determined on a dense set of functions in D.

Exercises

1-6. Use the formula (1-1) to calculate θ_C at $(0,0)$ for the vector fields

(i) $(u(x,y),v(x,y)) = (x^2 - y^2, 2xy)$

(ii) $(u(x,y),v(x,y)) = (ax + by, cx + dy)$ and $ab - cd \neq 0$, where C is the circle $x^2 + y^2 = R^2$.

1-7. Prove that the index of a zero of the gradient of the harmonic function $U(x,y)$ in D is always a negative integer. (Hint: $\overline{f'(z)} = U_x(x,y) + iU_y(x,y)$)

1-8. Construct vectors $(u(x,y),v(x,y))$ with $\theta_C/2\pi$ any integer; positive, negative or zero. (Hint: consider z^n, $\bar{z}^n$; $n = 0, 1, 2, \ldots$.)

1-9. If C is a closed level curve of the analytic function f, $C = \{z \mid |f(z)| = c\}$, with $f'(z) \neq 0$ on C, show that

$f(z)$ has at least one zero in C.

§1-3. SOME GENERAL PROBLEMS OF NONLINEAR ANALYSIS

The previous two sections were devoted to particular nonlinear problems. We now turn to a survey of general problems in nonlinear analysis, many of which will be taken up in the subsequent chapters. In analogy with the previous remarks on analytic functions we consider three interrelated classes of problems:

(i) problems concerning the real solutions of nonlinear systems of equations

(ii) problems concerning nonlinear mappings

(iii) problems concerning the real critical points of real-valued functions.

(i) Systems of nonlinear equations are classified in increasing order of generality as linear, algebraic, analytic, differentiable or continuous depending on whether the individual equations of the system depend on their arguments in a linear, polynomial, analytic, differentiable or continuous manner. Furthermore the well-posedness of such systems is often the primary center of interest. Well-posed systems of equations have precisely one solution which depends continuously on the given data of the system. However, many specific nonlinear problems arising in the study of nature, or in mathematics proper, do not possess this property of well-posedness, and so other qualitative features of a given system come to the fore. Among such problems are:

(a) <u>the theory of linearization</u>, namely what properties of a given system of arbitrary equations can be predicted from a complete knowledge of the properties of an associated linear system?

(b) the more general <u>theory of perturbation</u>, namely a description of the qualitative changes in the structure of the solutions of a system of equations produced by the addition of a small term to the equations

(c) <u>the theory of bifurcation</u> in which one considers the changes in the number of solutions of the system of equations $F_\lambda(x) = 0$ depending continuously on a parameter λ, as the parameter varies

(d) the determination of nonlinear invariants for a system of equations which give some idea of the structure of the solution of the system or more generally even the existence of some special solution of the given system. These invariants should have the property that small changes in the system of equations produce only small changes in the invariants

(e) <u>the local analysis of nonlinear systems of equa-</u>

<u>tions</u>, namely the determination of the structure of the solutions of the given system of equations with the restriction that the solutions under consideration should be contained in a small neighborhood of a given point.

(f) <u>the global analysis of nonlinear systems</u> in which one determines the totality of solutions of a nonlinear system and divides such solutions into classes with common properties

(ii) Nonlinear mappings are often separated into homotopy classes. Two mappings $h_0(x)$ and $h_1(x)$ with range Y and domain X are homotopic if there is a continuous mapping $H(x,t): X \times [0,1] \to Y$ such that $h_0(x) = H(x,0)$ and $h_1(x) = H(x,1)$. Homotopy is thus an equivalence relation between maps (always assumed to be continuous) with range Y and domain X, and the respective equivalence classes are called homotopy classes. The set of homotopy classes can often be given an algebraic structure which, in turn, enables computable nonlinear invariants relevant to describing qualitative features of nonlinear mappings. The advantage of this approach is that a given problem can be simplified by considering an equivalent homotopic one which possesses more readily computable nonlinear invariants. What are some of these qualitative features of nonlinear mappings? First the existence and structure of fixed points for the mapping of a space into itself. Secondly the determination of conditions guaranteeing the univalence (that is, one-to-one ness) of mappings. Next the determination of the conjugacy of mappings f, g; namely the existence of an invertible mapping h such that $f = h^{-1}gh$; and lastly, the related study of the structural stability of a class of mappings between the spaces X and Y which, roughly expressed, is that all the topological properties of each mapping in the class are left invariant under small perturbations and the class itself is dense in the family of all mappings between X and Y.

(iii) A continuous real-valued function $f(x)$ defined on a compact set X attains its maximum and minimum. More generally, if $f(x)$ is differentiable in some sense, we may try to investigate properties of the critical points of this function, that is points where the derivative of f is zero. For example, if $f(x_1,\ldots,x_n)$ is a continuously differentiable function of n real variables which has distinct relative minima at two different points, grad $f = (f_{x_1},\ldots,f_{x_n})$ vanishes at some other point provided $f(x_1,\ldots,x_n) \to \infty$ as $|x| \to \infty$. (See Section 2-3.) On the other hand the geometric properties of the compact set X sometimes bear an interesting relationship to the critical points of $f(x)$. For example, in the first section of this chapter we found for homogeneous polynomials $f(x_1,x_2,x_3)$ defined over the complex projective plane, that the critical points were called singular points (because of their geometric significance). Indeed a knowledge of the genus of the curve Γ defined by $f(x_1,x_2,x_3) = 0$ turns out to be a geometric invariant of Γ and in addition yields results on the distribution of the singular points of Γ. More generally, the following questions are of importance

(a) <u>the classification of critical points</u> on compact sets X with relation to the geometric properties of X.

(b) <u>the stability of critical points</u> under perturbation of the set X and/or the function $f(x)$.

(c) <u>the geometric invariants</u> of the set X that guarantee the existence of critical points of $f(x)$ of various types. These questions are closely related to problems in the classical calculus of variations, although such studie often require the introduction of infinite dimensional techniques.

Exercises

1-10. Let $f_i(x_1,\ldots,x_n) = 0$ $(i = 1,\ldots,n)$ be n linear functions in n unknowns in $\mathbb{R}^n$. Prove that the condition $\det|\partial f_i/\partial x_j| \neq 0$ makes the system well-posed.

1-11. Prove that the solutions of a polynomial equation in one variable depend continuously on its coefficients.

1-12. Suppose that $f(x_1,\ldots,x_n)$ is a real-valued twice differentiable convex function. Find conditions on f that make the system $f_{x_i} = 0$ $(i = 1,\ldots,n)$ well-posed.

1-13. Consider the system

$$x = \lambda[x + (x^2 - y^2)]$$
$$y = 2\lambda[y - 2xy]$$

(a) Compare the real and complex solutions and investigate their dependence on the parameter λ.

(b) Show that the real solutions can be regarded as the critical points of some real-valued function $F(x,y)$ on the sphere $x^2 + y^2 = R^2$. Investigate the situation as $R \to 0$.

1-14. Consider the system

$$x = \lambda[x + y(x^2 + y^2)]$$
$$y = \lambda[y - x(x^2 + y^2)]$$

(a) Investigate all real and complex solutions of this system with respect to their dependence on λ.

(b) Show that the solutions of the system cannot be regarded as the critical points of some real-valued function $F(x,y)$.

§1-4. APPLICATIONS OF NONLINEAR PROBLEMS

One of the fascinating aspects of nonlinear analysis is the unity it brings to a surprising variety of diverse problems in science. Nonlinear phenomenon arise naturally in geometry, physical science, economics, the life sciences, and ordinary and partial differential equations. Each specific area has a particularly interesting combination of nonlinear problems associated with it. These are most easily explained by examples.

For brevity, we limit ourselves to two significant cases

in the theory of ordinary and partial differential equations.

(i) The qualitative theory of dynamical systems. The study of the differential equations of the dynamics of rigid bodies can be traced back to Galileo and Newton. During the eighteenth and nineteenth centuries these equations formed an object of study of many of the foremost mathematicians including Lagrange, Hamilton and Jacobi. With the work of Poincaré and Liapunov at the turn of the century the new epoch of the qualitative theory of these differential equations began. Instead of attempting to devise explicit formulas for the solutions of the given equations, one attempted systematicall to describe the various solutions by their geometric properties.

For example, among the most striking features of nature is periodicity. Jacobi showed that the study of periodic motions of dynamical systems can be reduced to the geometric study of closed geodesics on a manifold $\mathfrak{M}$ with prescribed metric. These geodesics are curves $\zeta(t)$ on $\mathfrak{M}$ (for $-\infty < t < \infty$) which are critical points of the arc-length functional on $\mathfrak{M}$, such that $\zeta(t)$ is a periodic function of t. If the manifold $\mathfrak{M}$ has a homotopy class of curves not deformable to a point, (i.e. the fundamental group $\pi_1(\mathfrak{M}) \neq$ C one can guarantee the existence of a nontrivial periodic soltion for the associated dynamical system. This fact is obtained by noting that the curve with minimal arc length over all closed curves in the homotopy class is the required closed geodesic. However this result does not give any idea about the totality of closed geodesics on $\mathfrak{M}$, or whether the closed geodesics are dense in the family of all geodesics on $\mathfrak{M}$, or how to partition the closed geodesics into distinct equivalence classes. These are some of the problems studied by Poincaré and later by G. D. Birkhoff. Here they found that in the two-dimensional case the geometric properties of the manifold $\mathfrak{M}$ play a crucial role. Later M. Morse extended many of these ideas to n-dimensional compact manifolds, however many of the n-dimensional analogues of the results of Poincaré and Birkhoff have yet to be discovered. Nonetheless, the problems centered around dynamical systems are still in the forefront of mathematical research as witnessed in the recent articles of V. Arnold, J. Moser, and S. Smale.

(ii) The qualitative theory of boundary value problems. It was Fourier who in 1822 first saw that the study of the partial differential equations arising in nature requires the introduction of infinite dimensional concepts into analysis. Furthermore, at about the same time it was observed that the famous problem concerning the existence of solutions of the boundary value problem for Laplace's equation, $u_{xx} + u_{yy} = 0$, over a bounded domain D in the x,y plane could be studied as the minimization of the integral $\iint_D (u_x^2 + u_y^2)\, dx\, dy$ over the countably infinite dimensional space of functions $\{u\}$ which possess partial derivatives in some sense and take on the prescribed boundary values. This became known as Dirichlet's principle. Nonetheless the rigorous mathematical treatment of these problems and their nonlinear analogues waited until the turn of the century for adequate development. It was then that S. Bernstein, I. Fredholm and D. Hilbert separately gave important impetus to the problems of elliptic partial differential equations by demonstrating that

(a) the associated boundary value problems could be treated successfully by converting them into integral equations

(b) the minimization of the Dirichlet integral can be correctly carried out in a completely logical and consistent manner

(c) with an appropriate definition of ellipticity, many linear and nonlinear elliptic partial differential equations in the plane have analytic solutions, as does its simplest prototype: the Laplace equation

(d) nonlinear elliptic partial differential equations can be studied by means of the growth properties of their coefficients; and if these growth properties are sufficiently restricted, the associated boundary value problems have solutions independent of the size or shape of the domain G in the plane.

Abstractions of many of these results initiated the theory of linear equations in an infinite number of dimensions which was brilliantly formalized by S. Banach and F. Riesz into functional analysis. In the years before the Second World War the above developments led to many important insights in the theory of linear and nonlinear partial differential equations. One far reaching and interesting idea in this regard (developed by J. Schauder) was the successful treatment of the existence problems of a large class of nonlinear partial differential equations by means of the so-called fixed point theorems of abstract analysis. Another stride forward was made with the advent of various theorems of generalized differentiation. Thus one could speak of solutions of equations which were not differentiable in the classical sense, and in this broader context many previously difficult questions began to fall into a consistent pattern. In particular, one could define "generalized solutions" of many problems described by nonlinear partial differential equations. These generalized solutions could in turn be reformulated in terms of solutions of an operator equation in a Hilbert space. Then the results of abstract analysis could be applied to describe the qualitative features of these solutions. In many cases the regularity theorems of elliptic partial differential equations show that "generalized solutions" are indeed sufficiently smooth to satisfy the given problem in the pointwise (classical) sense.

Great advances continue to be made in the area of partial differential equations, and the insights obtained are permeating many other branches of mathematics and its applications such as algebraic geometry, the theory of several complex variables, and mathematical physics.

Bibliography

1. R. J. Walker, Algebraic Curves, Dover Publications, New York, 1962.

2. T. Skolem, Diophantische Gleichungen, Chelsea Publications, New York, 1950.

3. T. Nagell, Introduction to Number Theory, J. Wiley, New York, 1951.

CHAPTER 2

FINITE DIMENSIONAL SYSTEMS IN $\mathbb{R}^n$

In this chapter we study some properties of the qualitative theory of the structure of the real solutions of the system

$$f_i(x_1,\ldots,x_n) = 0 \qquad (i = 1,\ldots,n) \qquad (2\text{-}1)$$

where $(x_1,\ldots,x_n)$ denotes a point in real n-dimensional Euclidean space $\mathbb{R}^n$.

Of course, the example $x_i^2 + 1 = 0 \quad (i = 1,\ldots,n)$ shows that to give content and interest to our study we must impose restrictions on the functions $f_i(x_1,\ldots,x_n)$. We shall not assume that the functions f_i are real analytic or even infinitely differentiable in which cases more specialized facts are known. See [1]. Indeed we begin by assuming merely that the functions f_i are continuous. Consistent with the approach mentioned in Chapter 1, we begin in Section 2-1 by defining an invariant useful both in classifying all systems of the form (2-1) and in giving information concerning the structure of their real solutions, the so-called degree of the mapping f. In Section 2-2, we study gradient systems of functions, that is systems that can be written $F_{x_i} = f_i$ $(i = 1,\ldots,n)$ or in vector form grad F = f, where $F(x_1,\ldots,x_n)$ is some real-valued continuously differentiable function. The solutions of such systems (2-1) are the critical points of $F(x_1,\ldots,x_n)$, and thus we are led to a study of the classification of the critical points of a real-valued function. The chapter ends with the consideration of a special but important case, namely systems of equations deformable to gradient systems.

§2-1. THE DEFINITION OF DEGREE OF A MAPPING

We now generalize to n dimensions the ideas centering about the principle of the argument mentioned in Section 1-2. Let $f_i(x_1,\ldots,x_n)$ $(i = 1,\ldots,n)$ be n continuous functions of the variables $(x_1,\ldots,x_n)$, and consider $f = (f_1,\ldots,f_n)$ as defining a mapping from real Euclidean n-space $\mathbb{R}^n$ into itself. Our first objective is to classify all such mappings by an integer invariant called the degree of the mapping f, with the property that two functions that are "near" each other in some sense are assigned the same integer. This can be carried out in various equivalent ways.

(i) The analytic definition. Denote by $C(\bar{D})$ the set of continuous vector-valued functions defined on $\bar{D} \subset \mathbb{R}^n$ with the topology of uniform convergence, and by $C'(\bar{D})$ the subset of continuously differentiable vector-valued functions on $\bar{D}$, where D is a bounded open set in $\mathbb{R}^n$. We attempt to define a measure of the number of solutions of $f(x) = p$ in D by an integer $d(f,p,D)$ which depends continuously on both f and p. This integer is called the degree of the mapping f relative to the point p and the set D. The idea is to first define $d(f,p,D)$ on a dense set of functions f in $C(\bar{D})$ and on a dense set of points $p \in D$, then to extend the definition to all points in D and all functions in $C(\bar{D})$ by a limiting process. Throughout we assume that $f(x) = p$ has no solutions for $x \in \partial D$. The definition then proceeds very directly by counting the algebraic number of solutions of $f(x) = p$ in D, in the following three steps:

Step I. Suppose $f \in C'(\bar{D})$ and the Jacobian determinant of f, $\det J_f(x) = \det(\partial f_i/\partial x_i)$, does not vanish at any point x in the solution set $\{x | x \in D,\ f(x) = p\}$, then we define

$$d(f,p,D) = \sum_{x \in f^{-1}(p)} \operatorname{sgn} \det J_f(x)$$

This number is a finite integer as the set $f^{-1}(p)$ is discrete by the Implicit Function Theorem and as this discrete set has no limit point in the compact set $\bar{D}$.

Step II. To define $d(f,p,D)$ for functions $f \in C'(\bar{D})$ whose solution set contains some x where the Jacobian determinant $\det J_f(x) = 0$, we shall prove a special case of a result of A. Sard to the effect that if $B = \{x | \det J_f(x) = 0\}$, then $f(B)$ has an empty interior in $\mathbb{R}^n$. Assuming the validity of Sard's theorem, since $p \in f(B)$, p may be approximated by points p_m whose solution sets contain only x at which $\det J_f(x) \neq 0$. Thus we define $d(f,p,D) = \lim_{m \to \infty} d(f,p_m,D)$. (This definition is justified provided, it is independent of the approximating sequence p_m, the limit exists and is finite.)

Step III. To define the degree for all continuous functions $f \in C(\bar{D})$, we note that $C'(\bar{D})$ is dense in $C(\bar{D})$. Thus suppose $f_m \in C'(\bar{D})$ with $f_m \to f$ uniformly in $\bar{D}$. Then we define $d(f,p,D) = \lim_{m\to\infty} d(f_m,p,D)$. (Again this definition is justified provided it is independent of the particular approximating sequence f_m and a finite limit exists.)

We now proceed to a proof of the result mentioned in Step II.

LEMMA 2-1. (<u>A special case of Sard's theorem</u>) <u>Let</u> A <u>be any open set in</u> $\mathbb{R}^n$ <u>and</u> $f: A \to \mathbb{R}^n$ <u>be any continuously differentiable mapping</u>. <u>Denote by</u> $B = \{x | x \in A, \det J_f(x) = 0\}$, <u>then</u> $f(B)$ <u>has empty interior</u>.

<u>Proof</u>. The result is clear for linear mappings, for suppose $f(x) = ax + b$. If the determinant of the matrix a, $\det a$, is not zero, then $f(B) = \phi$, the empty set. On the other hand, if $\det a = 0$, then $B = A$ and the mapping f projects B into some hyperplane in $\mathbb{R}^n$, which certainly has empty interior in $\mathbb{R}^n$.

If f is not linear, consider an arbitrary cube $U \subset A$ of diameter Δ divided into "sufficiently small" subcubes U_k. (We shall show that the volume of $f(B)$ can be made arbitrarily small.) If $U_k \cap B \neq \phi$, we linearize f about any point in the intersection. If $U_k \cap B = \phi$, we omit that U_k from further consideration. More precisely, given $\epsilon > 0$, divide U into subcubes of diameter δ chosen so <u>small</u> that for any fixed $x \in U_k$ and all $y \in U_k$

$$|f(y) - f(x) - J_f(x)(y - x)| < \epsilon |x - y| \leq \epsilon\delta \quad (2\text{-}2)$$

The validity of (2-2) follows immediately from the Mean Value Theorem and the uniform continuity of the derivatives $(\partial f_i / \partial x_j)$ on U_k. For $x \in (B \cap U_k)$ consider the linearized mapping

$$L_x(y) = f(x) + J_f(x)(y - x)$$

L_x maps U_k into some hyperplane π_x and (2-2) implies the distance from π_x to $f(y)$ is at most $\epsilon\delta$. On the other hand, as $f(x)$ is continuously differentiable, x and $y \in U_k$ are not pulled too far apart by the mapping f. To obtain an estimate, let $\max_U|\partial f_i/\partial x_j| \leq M$, then by the Mean Value Theorem $|f(x) - f(y)| \leq M|x - y| \leq M\delta$. Therefore $f(U_k)$ lies inside a region, between two parallel slices of a sphere, whose volume is $K_n(2\epsilon\delta)(M\delta)^{n-1}$, where K_n is a dimensional constant independent of δ. If there are N^n subcubes U_k, the total volume of all the $f(U_k)$ is at most $N^n K_n(2\epsilon\delta)(\delta M)^{n-1} = 2K_n M^{n-1}\delta^n N^n \epsilon = \tilde{K}\epsilon$. To complete the proof of the lemma , we show that $\tilde{K}$ can be chosen independently of δ and N. The result is clearly seen by noting that $\delta = \Delta/N$ and so $\tilde{K} = 2K_n M^{n-1}\Delta^n$. ||

The following two lemmas, whose proofs will be sketched shortly, justify Steps II and III in the above analytic definition.

LEMMA 2-2. <u>Suppose</u> (i) $f \in C^2(D) \cap C(\bar{D})$, (ii) $\det J_f(x) \neq 0$ <u>for</u> $x \in f^{-1}(p)$ <u>or</u> $f^{-1}(q)$ <u>and</u> (iii) $f(x) \neq p$ <u>for</u> $x \in \partial D$. <u>Then whenever</u> q <u>is sufficiently near</u> p, $d(f,q,D) = d(f,p,D)$

LEMMA 2-3. *Suppose* (i) $f, g \in C'(D) \cap C(\bar{D})$, (ii) $\det J_f(x) \neq 0$ *for* $x \in f^{-1}(p)$, *and* (iii) $f(x) \neq p$ for $x \in \partial D$. *Then whenever* g *is sufficiently close to* f *in the* C' *sense* (*that is*, *for* ϵ *sufficiently small*, $\sup_D\{|f - g| + \Sigma_{i=1}^n |f_{x_i} - g_{x_i}|\} < \epsilon$), $d(g,p,D) = d(f,p,D)$.

The justification of Step II follows immediately if Lemma 2-2 can be extended to functions $f \in C'(D)$, and this follows from Lemmas 2-2 and 2-3 by approximating a given function in $C'(D)$ by an appropriate C^2 function.

REMARK 2-4. *Lemma* 2-1 *implies that Lemma* 2-3 *holds without hypothesis* (ii).

The justification of Step III follows immediately if the above Remark can be extended to functions g close to f in the C sense (that is, $\sup_D |f - g| < \epsilon$). This can be accomplished by a "homotopy" argument as follows. Let $h(x,t) = tf + (1 - t)g$ for $t \in [0,1]$, and suppose that $h(x,t) \neq p$ for $x \in \partial D$. Then we define $t \sim t'$ if $d(h(x,t),p,D) = d(h(x,t'),p,D)$. " $\sim$ " is an equivalence relation. By the above Remark 2-4, the associated disjoint equivalence classes are open in the space $[0,1]$. Thus $[0,1]$ is a union of open sets; namely the open equivalence classes.

This contradicts the connectedness of $[0,1]$ unless there is exactly one equivalence class. Hence $0 \sim 1$ and $d(f,p,D) = d(g,p,D)$.

Finally we return to sketch the proof of the above lemmas.

Outline of proof of Lemma 2-2. First we prove that under the hypothesis of the lemma, $d(f,p,D)$ has the following integral representation (for ϵ sufficiently small)

$$d(f,p,D) = \int_D \psi_\epsilon(f(x)) J_f(x)\, dx$$

where $\psi_\epsilon(x)$ is a family of real-valued continuous functions which vanish outside a sphere Σ_ϵ of radius ϵ centered at p and such that $\int_{\Sigma_\epsilon} \psi_\epsilon = 1$. Indeed, by hypothesis (ii) $f^{-1}(p) = \{x_1,\ldots,x_k\}$ is a finite set and, for ϵ sufficiently small there is a neighborhood $N_\epsilon(x_i)$ of each x_i $(i = 1, \ldots, k)$ mapped homeomorphically by f on Σ_ϵ, the sphere of radius ϵ about p. As $\psi_\epsilon(f(x))$ vanishes outside $\bigcup_{i=1}^k N_\epsilon(x_i)$,

$$\int_D \psi_\epsilon(f(x)) J_f(x)\, dx = \sum_{i=1}^k \int_{N_\epsilon(x_i)} \psi_\epsilon(f(x)) J_f(x)\, dx$$
$$= \sum_{i=1}^k \operatorname{sgn} \det J_f(x_i)$$

by the change of variables $y = f(x)$, noting $\int_{\Sigma_\epsilon} \psi_\epsilon(y)\, dy = 1$

Now, provided q is chosen so close to p that p and q are in the same component of $\mathbb{R}^n - f(\partial D)$,

$$d(f,q,D) = \int_D \psi_\epsilon(f(x) + q - p) J_f(x)\, dx$$

and it can be shown that provided $f \in C^2(D)$, see [5],

$$d(f,q,D) - d(f,p,D) = \int_D [\psi_\epsilon(f(x) + q - p) - \psi_\epsilon(f(x))] J_f(x)\, dx$$
$$= \int_{\mathbb{R}^n} \operatorname{div} u$$

where $u = (u_1,\ldots,u_n)$ is a continuously differentiable mapping of $\mathbb{R}^n$ into $\mathbb{R}^n$ which vanishes outside of D. Then, by the Divergence Theorem, $\int_{\mathbb{R}^n} \operatorname{div} u = 0$, and $d(f,p,D) = d(f,q,D)$. ||

<u>Outline of proof of Lemma</u> 2-3. By hypotheses (i) - (iii), $f(x) = p$ has a finite number of solutions $x_1,\ldots,x_k$. Let $\Sigma_{\delta_i}(x_i)$ be a sphere of radius δ_i about x_i. By choosing ϵ sufficiently small, one can show that $g(x) = p$ has exactly one solution $\bar{x}_i$ in each sphere $\Sigma_{\delta_i}(x_i)$ and no others; furthermore, at each solution $\operatorname{sgn} \det J_f(x_i) = \operatorname{sgn} \det J_g(\bar{x}_i)$. So $d(f,p,D) = \Sigma_{i=1}^k \operatorname{sgn} \det J_f(x_i) = \Sigma_{i=1}^k \operatorname{sgn} \det J_g(\bar{x}_i) = d(g,p,D)$. ||

Historically the analytic definition was preceded by the

following alternate definitions.

(ii) The definition by a surface integral. The direct generalization of formula (1-1) to n dimensions was carried out by L. Kronecker in 1869. To define an appropriate integral in n dimensions, we suppose the functions f_1, f_2, ..., f_n are continuously differentiable and have isolated zeros. Then the Kronecker integral relative to $f = (f_1, \ldots, f_n)$ and the simple case of a sphere S_ϵ at $x = 0$ is given by

$$d(f,0,S_\epsilon) = \frac{1}{K_{n-1}} \int_{\partial S_\epsilon} \frac{1}{|f|^n} \det \left| f, \frac{\partial f}{\partial s_1}, \ldots, \frac{\partial f}{\partial s_{n-1}} \right| ds_1 ds_2 \ldots ds_{n-1}$$

where $\det |f,\ldots,\partial f/\partial s_{n-1}|$ denotes the $n \times n$ determinant whose first row is $(f_1,\ldots,f_n)$ and whose $(i+1)$st row is $(\partial f_1/\partial s_i,\ldots,\partial f_n/\partial s_i)$. Here $s_1, s_2, \ldots, s_{n-1}$ are suitable coordinates defining ∂S_ϵ; K_{n-1} is the surface area of the sphere $|x| = 1$; S_ϵ is the solid sphere $\{x | x \in \mathbb{R}^n$ and $|x|^2 \leq \epsilon^2\}$; ∂S_ϵ is the positively oriented sphere $\{x | x \in \mathbb{R}^n$ and $|x|^2 = \epsilon^2\}$.

Provided that $f \neq 0$ on ∂S_ϵ, Kronecker proved that (a) this integral is always integer-valued; possibly negative, zero or positive: (b) the integer is a measure of the number of solutions of (2-1) inside S_ϵ; in particular if there are no solutions in S_ϵ the integral is 0. The reader is referred to an article of Hadamard [2], for an interesting exposition of this viewpoint.

(iii) The definition via homology groups. Another definition of the degree of a mapping was proposed by L. E. J. Brouwer. Let D be a bounded open set in $\mathbb{R}^n$ with boundary ∂D $(= \bar{D} - \text{int } D)$ which, for simplicity, we assume to be homeomorphic to S^{n-1} (the unit sphere in $\mathbb{R}^n$ with center at the origin). Then, provided the continuous functions $f_1, f_2, \ldots, f_n$ on $\bar{D}$ do not vanish simultaneously on ∂D, the continuous vector-valued function $\tilde{f} = (1/|f|)(f_1, f_2, \ldots, f_n)$ maps $\partial D \to S^{n-1}$. The degree of the mapping f is defined in the following way: the continuous mapping $\tilde{f}\colon \partial D \to S^{n-1}$ induces a group homomorphism $\tilde{f}_*$ between each homology group (with integer coefficients) $H_p(\partial D)$ and $H_p(S^{n-1})$. (See Appendix I.) As ∂D and S^{n-1} are homeomorphic and $H_{n-1}(S^{n-1}) = Z$ (the additive group of integers), $H_{n-1}(\partial D) = Z$. Furthermore since every group homomorphism of the additive group of integers into itself is of the form kz where k is some integer, $\tilde{f}_*(z) = kz$. This integer k is called the degree of f with respect to the origin and is denoted by $d(f,0,D)$ or $\deg \tilde{f}$. A well-known result in algebraic topology (Hopf's Theorem: see [3]) states that such mappings f can be classified up to homotopy equivalence by this integer k; possibly positive, negative or zero. In other words the degree of a mapping is the <u>only homotopy invariant</u> associated with continuous mappings of ∂D into S^{n-1}.

The basic properties of homology groups (stated in Appendix I) guarantee that (a) if $\tilde{f}$ is homotopic to $\tilde{g}$ on S^{n-1}, $\deg \tilde{f} = \deg \tilde{g}$; (b) if $\tilde{f}$ is the identity map, $\deg f = 1$; (c) if $\tilde{f}$ is a homeomorphism, $\deg f = \pm 1$; (d) if $\tilde{f}$ is not onto S^{n-1}, $\deg f = 0$.

In general, we define the degree $d(f,p,D)$ with respect to an arbitrary point $p \in \mathbb{R}^n$, provided $f(x) \neq p$ on ∂D, as the degree of the mapping $(f - p)/|f - p|: \partial D \to S^{n-1}$.

Since only the values of f on ∂D are required in the definition of $d(f,p,D)$, we shall also speak of $d(f,p,D)$ when the function f is given only on ∂D.[1]

Note that this definition insures the continuity of $d(f,p,D)$ as a function of $p \in \mathbb{R}^n$ and $f \in C(\bar{D})$ (with respect to uniform convergence).

The conceptual difficulties with this definition are considerably eliminated by the next paragraph.

The above definition may be extended to the case when D is an arbitrary bounded open set in $\mathbb{R}^n$. Indeed let h denote the stereographic projection of $S^n \to \mathbb{R}^n$, and denote

---

[1] It can be shown that all possible continuous extensions of f into D are homotopic, provided $f(x) \neq p$ for $x \in \partial D$.

its inverse by h^{-1}. Suppose f is a continuous mapping of $\bar{D} \to \mathbb{R}^n$ such that $f(x) \neq p$ for $x \in \partial D$. Then $f^* = h^{-1}fh$ is a mapping of $h^{-1}(\bar{D}) \subset S^n$ into S^n. This mapping may be extended to a mapping $f^{**}: S^n \to S^n$, by virtue of the Tietze Extension Theorem, in such a way that $f^{**}(x) \neq p$ on $f^{**}(\partial D)$. Furthermore, any two such mappings with this property are unique up to homotopy equivalence. As f^{**} is a continuous mapping of $S^n \to S^n$ we may define $d(f,p,D) = \deg f^{**}$. (See [4].)

Before ending this section it is important to note that the degrees computed by either definition (ii) or (iii) are equivalent. We state this result formally as follows:

THEOREM 2-5. _Let_ f _be a continuous mapping of the bounded domain_ $D \subset \mathbb{R}^n$ _into_ $\mathbb{R}^n$. _Suppose_ $f(x) \neq p$ _for_ $x \in \partial D$, _where_ p _is a point in_ $\mathbb{R}^n$, _and let_ $\tilde{d}(f,p,D)$ _be the degree defined by homology groups and_ $d(f,p,D)$ _be the degree determined by the analytic definition_ (i). _Then_ $d(f,p,D) = \tilde{d}(f,p,D)$.

The proof of this result requires a certain amount of algebraic topology and will be omitted here as it will not be used in the sequel. (See [6].)

Exercises

2-1. Let $f(z) = u(x,y) + iv(x,y)$ be a complex analytic function defined on a bounded domain D and its closure $\bar{D}$ in $\mathbb{R}^2$, where $z = x + iy$ and $i^2 = -1$. Suppose $f(z) \neq p$ for $z \in \partial D$. Prove $d(f,p,D) \geq 0$, where f denotes the mapping $(x,y) \to (u,v)$.

2-2. Suppose $f(z_1,z_2,\ldots,z_n)$ is a continuous function defined on a bounded domain D and its closure $\bar{D}$ mapping $\mathbb{C}^n$ into itself. Let

$$f(z_1,z_2,\ldots,z_n) = u(x_1,y_1,x_2,y_2,\ldots,x_n,y_n) + iv(x_1,y_1,x_2,y_2,\ldots,x_n,y_n)$$

where $z_j = x_j + iy_j$, and $i^2 = -1$, $u = (u_1,u_2,\ldots,u_n)$ and $v = (v_1,v_2,\ldots,v_n)$. Then f may be regarded as a continuous mapping of $\bar{D} \to \mathbb{R}^{2n}$, namely

$$f: (x_1,y_1,\ldots,x_n,y_n) \to (u_1,v_1,\ldots,u_n,v_n)$$

Suppose that u_k and v_k satisfy the following "Cauchy-Riemann equations"

$$\partial u_k/\partial x_j = \partial v_k/\partial y_j, \quad \text{and} \quad \partial u_k/\partial y_j = -\partial v_k/\partial x_j$$

for $(j,k = 1,\ldots,n)$. Prove that $d(f,p,D) \geq 0$ provided it is defined.

2-3. Let $f = ax + b$ be a linear mapping of $\mathbb{R}^n$ into $\mathbb{R}^n$, where a is an $n \times n$ matrix. Prove by definition (ii) of degree, that if $f(x_0) = p$ then

$$d(f,p,\Sigma_\epsilon) = \begin{cases} 1 & \text{if } \det a > 0 \\ -1 & \text{if } \det a < 0 \end{cases}$$

where Σ_ϵ is a sphere of any radius ϵ centered about x_0 in $\mathbb{R}^n$. What happens if $\det a = 0$?

2-4. Suppose $f(x)$ is a continuously differentiable mapping of a small sphere Σ_ϵ in $\mathbb{R}^n$ into $\mathbb{R}^n$ such that (i)

$f(x) = p$ at the center x_0 of Σ_ϵ, (ii) the Jacobian determinant of f, $\det J_f(x)$, is nonzero for $x \in \Sigma_\epsilon$, and (iii) $f(x) = p$ has no solutions $x \in \partial\Sigma_\epsilon$. Prove by the previous problem and the definition (ii) of degree that

$$d(f,p,\Sigma_\epsilon) = \operatorname{sgn} \det J_f(x_0)$$

(Hint. Use the Mean Value Theorem and the homotopy invariance of degree.)

§2-2. SOME PROPERTIES OF THE DEGREE OF A MAPPING

Here we state the basic properties of the function $d(f,p,D)$ as well as indicate the proofs of these results by means of the analytic definition discussed in the last section. Let $f: \bar{D} \to \mathbb{R}^n$ be a continuous mapping and $f(x) = p$ have no solutions $x \in \partial D$. Here D denotes an arbitrary bounded open set in $\mathbb{R}^n$.

Invariance properties

2-6. (Boundary Value Dependence) $d(f,p,D)$ *is uniquely determined by the action of* $f(x)$ *on* ∂D.

2-7. (Homotopy Invariance) *Suppose* $H(x,t) = p$ *has no solution* $x \in \partial D$ *for any* $t \in [0,1]$ *then* $d(H(x,t),p,D)$ *is a constant independent of* $t \in [0,1]$ *provided* $H(x,t)$ *is a continuous function of* x *and* t.

2-8. (Continuity) $d(f,p,D)$ *is a continuous function of* $f \in C(\bar{D})$ (*with respect to uniform convergence*) *and of* $p \in D$.

2-9. (Poincaré-Bohl) *If the vectors* $f(x) - p$ *and*

$g(x) - p$ *never point in opposite directions for* $x \in \partial D$, *then* $d(f,p,D) = d(g,p,D)$ *provided each is defined*.

Proofs. 2-8 is an immediate consequence of the analytic definition of $d(f,p,D)$. 2-7 is then a consequence of 2-8, as $h(t) = d(H(x,t),p,D)$ is a continuous function of t and because $h(t)$ is integer-valued, $h(t)$ must be constant. 2-6 follows immediately by considering the homotopy $H(x,t) = tf + (1 - t)\tilde{f}$ where $f \equiv \tilde{f}$ on ∂D. Similarly 2-9 is obtained by means of the homotopy $H(x,t) = t(f(x) - p) + (1 - t)(g(x) - p)$. ||

Arithmetic Properties

2-10. (*Domain Decomposition*) *If* $\{D_i\}$ *is a finite collection of disjoint open subsets of* D *and* $f(x) \neq p$ *for* $x \in (\bar{D} - \cup_i D_i)$ *then* $d(f,p,D) = \Sigma_i\, d(f,p,D_i)$.

2-11. (*Cartesian product formula*) *If* $p \in D \subset \mathbb{R}^n$, $p' \in D' \subset \mathbb{R}^m$ *and* $f: D \to \mathbb{R}^n$, $g: D' \to \mathbb{R}^m$, *then* $d((f,g),(p,p'),D \times D') = d(f,p,D) \cdot d(g,p',D')$ *provided the right hand side is defined*.

2-12. *If* $f(x) \neq p$ *in* $\bar{D}$, *then* $d(f,p,D) = 0$.

2-13. (*Odd mappings*) *Let* D *be a symmetric domain about the origin, and* $f(-x) = -f(x)$ *on* ∂D, *with* $f: D \to \mathbb{R}^n$ *and* $f(x) \neq 0$ *on* ∂D, *then* $d(f,0,D)$ *is an odd integer*.

<u>Proofs</u>. These arithmetic properties of the degree follow immediately from the analytic defintion. The ideas involved can be simply expressed. Each property is proved for a dense set of points $p \in D$ and functions $f \in C(\bar{D})$ and then extended to all points $p \in D$ and functions $f \in C(\bar{D})$ by a limiting process. Throughout we suppose $f \in C'(\bar{D})$ and for $x \in (D \cap f^{-1}(p))$, $\det J_f(x) \neq 0$. Then to demonstrate 2-10 we note that

$$d(f,p,D) = \sum_{x \in f^{-1}(p)} \operatorname{sgn} \det J_f(x) = \sum_i \sum_{x \in D_i \cap f^{-1}(p)} \operatorname{sgn} \det J_f(x)$$

$$= \sum_i d(f,p,D_i)$$

To prove 2-11, note

$$d((f,g),(p,p'),D \times D') = \sum_{\substack{x \in f^{-1}(p) \\ x' \in g^{-1}(p')}} \operatorname{sgn} \det \begin{vmatrix} J_f(x) & 0 \\ 0 & J_g(x') \end{vmatrix}$$

$$= \{ \sum_{x \in f^{-1}(p)} \operatorname{sgn} \det J_f(x) \} \{ \sum_{x' \in g^{-1}(p')} \operatorname{sgn} \det J_g(x') \}$$

$$= d(f,p,D) \cdot d(g,p',D')$$

The proof of 2-12 is immediate. A short proof of the result 2-13 on odd mappings can be given provided that f is continuously differentiable and the Jacobian determinant of f does not vanish at any solution of $f(x) = 0$ in D. Indeed as f is an odd mapping, the solutions of $f(x) = 0$ can be grouped in pairs $(\bar{x}, -\bar{x})$ together with $\bar{x} = 0$. Furthermore, the oddness of f also insures that the Jacobian determinants of f at $x = \bar{x}$ and $x = -\bar{x}$ are necessarily equal and by assumption, they are nonzero. Thus by the analytic definition of degree

$$\begin{aligned} d(f,0,D) &= \sum_{\bar{x} \in f^{-1}(0)} \operatorname{sgn} \det J_f(\bar{x}) \\ &= \operatorname{sgn} \det J_f(0) + \text{even integer} \\ &= \text{odd integer} \end{aligned}$$

The interested reader may supply a somewhat longer proof along these lines to yield the general result. ||

The degree of a mapping is fundamental in clarifying the idea of the index of a mapping mentioned in Chapter 1, Section 1-2. Indeed if the solutions of $f(x) = p$ are isolated in $\mathbb{R}^n$, we define the index of f at a solution x_0 of $f(x) = p$ as the degree $d(f(x) - p, 0, \Sigma_\epsilon)$ where $\Sigma_\epsilon = \{x \mid |x - x_0| \le \epsilon\}$ and ϵ is chosen so small that x_0 is the only solution of $f(x) = p$ in or on Σ_ϵ. We write $i(x_0, f(x) - p) = d(f(x) - p, 0, \Sigma_\epsilon)$ to emphasize that this definition is independent of ϵ, provided ϵ is sufficiently small. Furthermore, from the decomposition of domain property of $d(f,p,D)$ we have:

2-14. <u>If the solutions of</u> $f(x) = p$ <u>are isolated on</u> D <u>and</u> $f(x) \neq p$ <u>on</u> ∂D <u>then</u> $d(f,p,D) = \Sigma_{x_j \in f^{-1}(p)} i(x_j, f(x) - p)$.

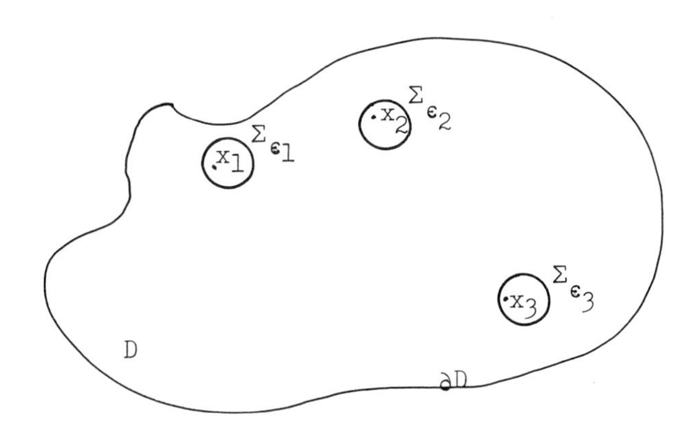

Figure 3. The degree $d(f,p,D)$ is the sum of the indices:
$d(f,p,D) = \Sigma_{j=1}^{3} d(f,p,\Sigma_{\epsilon_j}) = \Sigma_{j=1}^{3} i(x_j, f(x) - p)$

The properties of the degree of a mapping provide interesting information concerning the solutions of the system $f_i(x_1,\ldots,x_n) = p_i$ where $f_i(x)$ are continuous real-valued functions in $\bar{D}$ and the p_i are real numbers. Some results in this direction are:

2-15. <u>If</u> $d(f,p,D) \neq 0$, <u>then the equation</u> $f(x) = p$ <u>has solutions in</u> D.

2-16. (<u>Brouwer Fixed Point Theorem</u>) <u>Let</u> $f\colon \Sigma \to \Sigma$ <u>be a continuous mapping of the sphere</u> $\Sigma = \{x \mid |x| \leq 1\}$ <u>into itself, then there is a point</u> $x_0 \in \Sigma$ <u>with</u> $x_0 = f(x_0)$.

2-17. (<u>Borsuk-Ulam Theorem</u>) <u>Let</u> $f: S^n \to \mathbb{R}^n$ <u>be a continuous mapping, then there is a point</u> $x_0 \in S^n$ <u>with</u> $f(x_0) = f(-x_0)$.

To prove 2-15, we note that as $d(f,p,D) \neq 0$, $f(x) = p$ necessarily has solutions in D by property 2-7 above. To prove 2-16, suppose that $f(x) = x$ has no solutions $x \in \partial\Sigma$ and $d(x - f(x),0,\Sigma) = 0$, then we shall obtain a contradiction by showing $d(x - f(x),0,\Sigma) = 1$. Indeed under the hypothesis, the homotopy $H(x,t) = x - tf(x)$ has no zero on $\partial\Sigma$ and thus $d(x - f(x),0,\Sigma) = d(x - tf(x),0,\Sigma) = d(x,0,\Sigma) = 1$. To prove 2-17, we use the property 2-13 of degree. Consider the mapping

$$\tilde{f} = (f_1(x) - f_1(-x),f_2(x) - f_2(-x),\ldots,f_n(x) - f_n(-x),0)$$

of $S^n \to \mathbb{R}^{n+1}$. Assume for each $x \in S^n$, $f_i(x) \neq f_i(-x)$ for some $i = 1,\ldots,n$; then $d(\tilde{f},0,\Sigma)$ is defined and as $\tilde{f}$ is odd, $\tilde{f}$ has odd degree and in particular nonzero degree. Consider the mapping $\tilde{g} = (0,0,\ldots,0,1)$, mapping $S^n \to \mathbb{R}^{n+1}$. The $d(\tilde{g},0,\Sigma) = 0$ while the homotopy $H(x,t) = t\tilde{g} + (1 - t)\tilde{f} \neq 0$ on S^n. Therefore $d(\tilde{f},0,\Sigma) = d(H(x,t),0,\Sigma) = d(\tilde{g},0,\Sigma) = 0$. ||

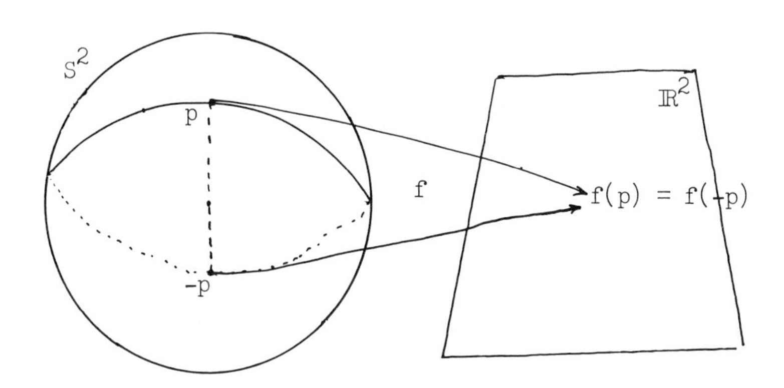

Figure 4. The Borsuk-Ulam Theorem for $n = 2$.

Now we turn to two problems concerning continuous mappings $f = (f_1, f_2, \ldots, f_n)$ defined on spheres S^{n-1} which depend on the parity of n. First the question of invariant directions on S^{n-1} under f and secondly the question of the existence of nonvanishing tangent vector fields on S^{n-1}: A nonvanishing tangent vector field $v(x)$ on S^{n-1} is a mapping $v(x)\colon S^{n-1} \to \mathbb{R}^n$ such that $v(x) \cdot x = 0$ and $v(x) \neq 0$. A simple approach to both problems is provided by noting that the degree of the antipodal map $f(x) = -x$ in $\Sigma = \{x \mid |x| \leq 1\}$ with respect to the origin is $(-1)^n$. Thus we have the following two results:

EXAMPLE 2-18. <u>Suppose</u> $f(x)\colon S^{n-1} \to \mathbb{R}^n$ <u>does not vanish for</u> $x \in S^{n-1}$, <u>then if</u> n <u>is odd</u>, <u>the direction of some normal vector is left unchanged under</u> f (<u>apart from sign</u>), <u>that</u>

<u>is, there is some real number</u> $\lambda \neq 0$ <u>and some</u> $x_0 \in S^{n-1}$ <u>such that</u> $f(x_0) = \lambda x_0$.

<u>Proof</u>. Let $\Sigma = \{x \mid |x| \leq 1\}$. Then by hypothesis $d(f,0,\Sigma)$ is defined. If n is odd, by the homotopy invariance property, one of the homotopies $H_1(x,t) = tf(x) + (1 - t)x$ and $H_2(x,t) = tf(x) + (1 - t)(-x)$ must vanish for some $t_0 \in (0,1)$ and $x_0 \in S^{n-1}$. For if both do not vanish, $d(f,0,\Sigma) = d(x,0,\Sigma) = 1$ and $d(f,0,\Sigma) = d(-x,0,\Sigma) = -1$. But if one of the homotopies vanishes $f(x_0) = \lambda x_0$ for some real and nonzero λ. ||

EXAMPLE 2-19. <u>A nonvanishing tangent vector field exists on</u> S^{n-1} <u>if and only if</u> n <u>is even</u>.

<u>Proof</u>. If n is even, $n = 2m$, let $x = (x_1,x_2,\ldots,x_{2m-1},x_{2m})$ $\in S^{n-1}$ and set $v(x) = (x_2,-x_1,\ldots,x_{2m},-x_{2m-1})$ then $v(x)\cdot x = 0$ and $v(x) \neq 0$ for $x \in S^{n-1}$. On the other hand, suppose a tangent vector field $v(x)$ exists. Consider the homotopy $H(x,t) = x \cos \pi t - (v(x)/|v(x)|) \sin \pi t$. Then $H(x,0) = x$ and $H(x,1) = -x$. This homotopy is well-defined, as one easily computes $|H(x,t)| = 1$. Thus $d(-x,0,\Sigma)$ $= d(x,0,\Sigma) = 1$, but $d(-x,0,\Sigma) = (-1)^n$. Hence n must be even. ||

An interesting method of defining tangent vector fields

on spheres is to consider a system of ordinary differential equations:

$$x_i'(t) = f_i(x_1, x_2, \ldots, x_n) \quad (i = 1, 2, \ldots, n) \qquad (2\text{-}3)$$

where " ' " denotes differentiation with respect to t. Then if we consider for example the sphere $S^{n-1} = \{\Sigma_{i=1}^n x_i^2 = R^2\}$, we may differentiate with respect to t to obtain $\Sigma_{i=1}^n x_i x_i'(t) = 0$, that is the vector $(x_1'(t), \ldots, x_n'(t)) = x'(t)$ is a tangent vector field on S^{n-1}. The points where this vector field vanishes are precisely the zeros of the vector function $f = (f_1, f_2, \ldots, f_n)$, and such points are called stationary points of the system (2-3).

Let us consider the problem of obtaining a lower bound for the number of such stationary points. Clearly if n is odd, the result 2-19 above shows that such points must necessarily exist on S^{n-1}. As the Euler-Poincaré characteristic[2] of S^{n-1}, $\chi(S^{n-1}) = \{2$ if n is odd and 0 if n is even$\}$, we obtain the result that $\chi(S^n) = 0$ if and only if S^n admits a nonvanishing tangent vector field. In this form,

---

[2] The Euler-Poincaré characteristic $\chi(\mathfrak{M})$ can be computed directly from the homology groups of $\mathfrak{M}$: $\chi(\mathfrak{M}) = \Sigma_{i=1}^n (-1)^i R_i$; where R_i is the ith Betti number of $\mathfrak{M}$, that is the rank of the homology group $H_i(\mathfrak{M})$ with integer coefficients. (See Appendix I.)

the above result generalizes to an arbitrary compact differentiable manifold[3] $\mathfrak{M}$. Such a manifold is locally homeomorphic to Euclidean space and if a tangent vector field vanishe at isolated points on $\mathfrak{M}$, we may consider the index of the vector field at such points. One considers a small neighborhood U on $\mathfrak{M}$ enclosing at most one point p where the tangent vector field $v(x)$ vanishes. Then the index of $v(x)$ at p is defined and the following result holds:

THEOREM 2-20. (Hopf) Let $v(x)$ be a tangent vector field on a compact differentiable manifold $\mathfrak{M}$ which vanishes at isolated points of $\mathfrak{M}$. Then the sum of the indices at such isolated points (a) is independent of the vector field $v(x)$ and (b) is equal to the Euler-Poincaré characteristic of $\mathfrak{M}$, $\chi(\mathfrak{M})$. (Thus on any manifold $\mathfrak{M}$ with $\chi(\mathfrak{M}) \neq 0$, the system (2-3) has at least one stationary point.)

Proof. The proof of part (a) depends on the geometry of $\mathfrak{M}$ and so instead of proving it here, we refer to the proof of

---

[3] An n-dimensional manifold $\mathfrak{M}$ is defined to be a Hausdorff topological space together with a countable covering of $\mathfrak{M}$ by open sets $\{U_i\}$ and mappings $\{f_i\}$ such that (a) f_i is a homeomorphism from U_i onto an open subset of $\mathbb{R}^n$ and (b) whenever $U_i \cap U_j \neq 0$ the mapping $f_i f_j^{-1}$ is given by n differentiable functions with nonvanishing Jacobian.

Milnor [7]. The proof of part (b) is outlined in Exercise 2-21 of Section 2-4.

Exercises

2-5. Let $F(x_1,\dots,x_n) = \Sigma\, a_{ij}x_ix_j$ be a real nonsingular quadratic form with $a_{ij} = a_{ji}$. Prove that $i(\text{grad } F,0) = (-1)^\lambda$ where λ is the number of negative eigenvalues of the self-adjoint matrix (a_{ij}).

2-6. Let f be a continuous mapping of a bounded domain D of $\mathbb{R}^n$ into $\mathbb{R}^n$ with the property that for all $x \in \partial D$, $f(x)$ never points in the direction q ($\neq 0$), that is, $f(x) \neq kq$ for all real nonzero k. Then $d(f,0,D) = 0$.

2-7. (A result of Frobenius) Suppose A is an $n \times n$ matrix (a_{ij}) with $a_{ij} > 0$ for $(i,j = 1,\dots,n)$. Prove using the Brouwer Fixed Point Theorem, that A has a positive eigenvalue and a corresponding eigenvector $x = (x_1,x_2,\dots,x_n)$ with all $x_i \geq 0$ and some $x_j > 0$. [Hint: Let $|x| = |x_1| + |x_2| + \dots + |x_n|$ and consider the mapping $\tilde{A}(x) = Ax/|Ax|$ on the closed convex set $\partial\Sigma_1^+ = \{x \,|\, |x| = 1,\ x = (x_1,\dots,x_n),\ x_i \geq 0\ \ (i = 1,\dots,n)\}$.]

2-8. (On Coverings of Spheres) Suppose a family of closed sets $A_1,A_2,\dots,A_{n-1}$ covers S^{n-1}. Prove by means of the Borsuk-Ulam Theorem that some A_i contains a pair of antipodal points. (For a stronger result see Section 2-5.) [Hint: Consider the mapping $d\colon S^{n-1} \to \mathbb{R}^{n-1}$ given by $d(x) = (d_1(x),d_2(x),\dots,d_{n-1}(x))$ where $d_i(x)$ is the distance of x to A_i.]

2-9. (The Ham Sandwich Theorem) Prove, using the Borsuk-Ulam

Theorem, that it is always possible to bisect three measurable sets arbitrarily placed in $\mathbb{R}^3$ by one plane.

2-10. Define a nonvanishing tangent vector field on the torus $T^2 = \{(x_1,y_1,x_2,y_2) \mid x_i^2 + y_i^2 = 1 \quad (i = 1,2)\}$.

§2-3. GRADIENT SYSTEMS AND THEIR BASIC PROPERTIES

Let $F(x_1,\ldots,x_n)$ be a real-valued continuously differentiable function defined on $\mathbb{R}^n$. The solutions of the equations $F_{x_i} = 0 \quad (i = 1,\ldots,n)$ are called critical points of F. A system of functions $f_1,f_2,\ldots,f_n$ which can be represented by the formulae $f_i(x_1,\ldots,x_n) = F_{x_i}$ for some differentiable function $F(x_1,\ldots,x_n)$ is called a gradient system. Thus the zeros of a gradient system are the critical points of some differentiable function, and we shall study the structure of these zeros by means of the theory of critical points of real-valued functions.

We begin with a few introductory remarks:

LEMMA 2-21. Critical points are preserved under coordinate transformations.

Proof. Let $g\colon (x_1,\ldots,x_n) \to (g_1,\ldots,g_n)$ be any smooth one-one coordinate transformation, and the point $\bar{x} = (\bar{x}_1,\ldots,\bar{x}_n)$ be any critical point of F. Then $g(\bar{x})$ is a critical point of F in the new coordinate system. Indeed

$$(\partial F/\partial g_i) = \sum_{j=1}^{n} (\partial F/\partial x_j)(\partial g_i/\partial x_j)^{-1}$$

Conversely, any critical point of F in the new coordinate system is the image of a critical point in the $(x_1,\ldots,x_n)$ coordinates. ||

LEMMA 2-22. _A necessary and sufficient condition for a system_ $(f_1,\ldots,f_n)$ _to be a gradient system is_ $(\partial f_i/\partial x_j) = (\partial f_j/\partial x_i)$ $(i,j = 1,\ldots,n)$, _and if this condition is valid an appropriate function_ $F(x_1,\ldots,x_n)$ _is_

$$F(x_1,\ldots,x_n) = \sum_{i=1}^{n} \int_0^1 f_i(tx_1,\ldots,tx_n)x_i \, dt$$

Proof. The first part of the result is merely a condition that a line integral $\int_C$ be independent of the path C. Secondly, setting $F(0) = 0$, we have

$$F(x_1,\ldots,x_n) = \int_0^1 F_t(tx_1,tx_2,\ldots,tx_n) \, dt$$

$$= \sum_{i=1}^{n} \int_0^1 F_{x_i}(tx_1,\ldots,tx_n)x_i \, dt$$

$$= \sum_{i=1}^{n} \int_0^1 f_i(tx_1,\ldots,tx_n)x_i \, dt \quad ||$$

LEMMA 2-23. Let $f = (f_1,\ldots,f_n)$ be a continuously differentiable mapping of $\mathbb{R}^n$ into $\mathbb{R}^n$. Then the set S of solutions of the system of equations $f = 0$ coincides with the set of critical points of some real-valued function defined on $\mathbb{R}^{2n}$, provided $\det J_f(x) \neq 0$ on S.

Proof. Let a point in $\mathbb{R}^{2n}$ be denoted $(x_1,\ldots,x_n,y_1,\ldots,y_n) = (x,y)$. Define $F(x,y) = \Sigma_{i=1}^n f_i(x)y_i$. At a critical point of F, $F_{x_j} = F_{y_i} = 0$ $(i,j = 1,\ldots,n)$; that is $f_i(x_1,\ldots,x_n) = 0$ and $\Sigma_{i=1}^n (\partial f_i/\partial x_j)y_i = 0$. As $\det J_f(x) \neq 0$ on S, all critical points of F have $y \equiv 0$, and hence coincide with the zeros of the system $(f_1,\ldots,f_n)$. ||

(More generally, even if $J_f(x) = 0$ on S, in many cases we can represent the zeros of f as limits of critical points of a sequence of real-valued continuously differentiable functions.)

Now let us consider the question of what conditions to impose on a gradient system $(f_1,\ldots,f_n)$ to insure the associated critical points actually do exist. We shall be concerned with this question throughout the next few sections of this chapter. Here we shall give two preliminary results in this direction which are significant for our later work.

Let $F(x)$ be a continuously differentiable real-valued function defined on $\mathbb{R}^n$ satisfying the growth condition

$F(x) \to \infty$ as $|x| \to \infty$, then

2-24. $\inf_{\mathbb{R}^n} F(x)$ _is attained at_ $x = x_0$ _and_ x_0 _is a critical point of_ $F(x)$.

2-25. _If_ $F(x)$ _has two distinct isolated relative minima at_ $x = x_0$ _and_ x_1, _then_ $F(x)$ _has a further distinct critical point_.

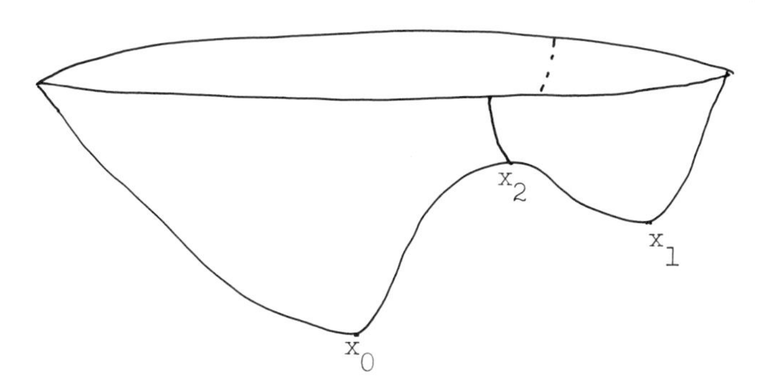

Figure 5. The graph of $z = F(x)$ illustrating a saddle point at x_2 between the relative minima x_0 and x_1.

Proof of 2-24. By hypothesis, for every number b there is a positive integer N_b such that $F(x) > b$ for $|x| \geq N_b$. Hence $\inf_{\mathbb{R}^n} F(x)$ is a finite number which we denote by a. Furthermore, as the sphere $S_{N_a} = \{x \mid |x| \leq N_a\}$ is compact in $\mathbb{R}^n$, $\inf_{\mathbb{R}^n} F(x)$ is attained at some point $x_0 \in S_{N_a}$, and by the choice of N_a this point lies inside S_{N_a}. Thus $\min_{\mathbb{R}^n} F(x) = F(x_0)$ and $\operatorname{grad} F(x_0) = 0$. ||

Proof of 2-25. Let $F(x)$ have two distinct relative minima at x_0 and x_1 and let $F(x_0) = a_0$ and $F(x_1) = a_1$. Then consider the class $[C]$ of compact connected sets C in $\mathbb{R}^n$ containing the points x_0 and x_1. Set

$$a = \inf_{[C]} \max_{C} F(x)$$

We shall establish the existence of another critical point x_2 with $F(x_2) = a$. Clearly $a > \max(a_0, a_1)$. Consider the straight line C^* joining x_0 and x_1 and let $R = \max_{C^*} F(x)$ Since $F(x) \to \infty$ as $|x| \to \infty$, there is an integer N such that $F(x) > R$ for $|x| \geq N$. Hence $\inf_{[C]} \max_C F(x)$ can only be achieved in the sphere $|x| \leq N$. Now consider a sequence of numbers $a_{C_1}, a_{C_2}, \ldots$ which are maximum values of F on C_1, $C_2, \ldots$, respectively, achieved at $x_{C_1}, x_{C_2}, \ldots$, such that $\lim_{m \to \infty} a_{C_m} = a$. Thus all $C_i \subset (|x| \leq N)$ for i sufficiently large. Let the limit set $\bar{C}$ be the set of points of accumulation of all sequences $\{x_i\}$, $x_i \in C_i$. $\bar{C}$ is known to be compact and connected and contains x_0 and x_1. Furthermore, a suitable subsequence which we again denote by x_{C_m} converges

$$x_{C_m} \to x_{\bar{C}} \quad \text{where} \quad x_{\bar{C}} \in \bar{C}$$

By continuity, $F(x_{\bar{C}}) = a$. In $[C]$, let C be the compact set $\{x | F(x) = a,\ x \in \bar{C}\}$. We show the existence of at least one point in C which is a critical point of F by supposing the contrary and obtaining a contradiction by continuously deforming the set $\bar{C}$ into a set $\bar{C}'$ with $\max_{\bar{C}'} F(x) < a$. To define such a transformation, suppose on C that $|\text{grad } F(x)| \geq 4\alpha > 0$, and thus on the slightly larger set C' not containing x_0 or x_1 whose points are at most a distance b from some point on C, $|\text{grad } F(x)| > 2\alpha$. The deformation of $\bar{C}$ to an appropriate $\bar{C}'$ will be carried out by leaving points outside C' unchanged and consistently decreasing $F(x)$ at points in C'. To this end we note that by the Mean Value Theorem and the uniform continuity of grad $F(x)$, on any compact set given $\delta > 0$,

$$F(x - tv) = F(x) - tv \cdot \text{grad } F(x) + t\tau(t)$$

with $|\tau(t)| < \delta$ provided $|t| \leq t_\delta$. Setting $v = \text{grad } F(x)$ and $\delta = \alpha^2$ on the compact set C' we have

$$F(x - tv) \leq F(x) - 4\alpha^2 t + t\alpha^2 = F(x) - 3\alpha^2 t$$

Thus $F(x)$ can be decreased on C' by deforming along gradient lines. We now show that such a deformation can be carried out continuously without affecting the value of $F(x)$ not in C'. To this end we cover C by spheres of radius b whose centers lie in C. Clearly all spheres lie in C'. By the compactness of C a finite number of spheres suffices in the covering and in each such sphere we consider the deformation

$$x' = x - t_\delta(b - r) \text{ grad } F(x)$$

where r denotes the distance of x to the center. Outside the sphere we set $x' = x$. Thus inside each sphere $F(x') < F(x)$. Performing a finite number of such transformations, one on each sphere of the finite subcovering, C' is transformed into itself and $\bar{C}$ is transformed continuously to a set $\bar{C}'$ on which $\max F(x) < a$, as only points in C' were affected by the transformation. Thus $\alpha > 0$ leads to a contradiction and C must contain a critical point. ||

So far we have considered critical points of a real-valued function $F(x)$ defined on all $\mathbb{R}^n$. As a prelude to later work in this chapter, we give brief consideration to the problem of critical points of functions satisfying a constraint of the form $g(x_1,\ldots,x_n) = 0$, where $g(x)$ is a real-valued smooth function defined on $\mathbb{R}^n$ and such that grad $g(x) \neq 0$ whenever $g(x) = 0$. Such constraints define a hypersurface $\mathfrak{M}$ in $\mathbb{R}^n$. Thus we consider $F(x)$ restricted to the hypersurface $\mathfrak{M}$ defined by $g(x) = 0$, and we find the critical points of $F(x)$ there. In this connection we recall the following result from advanced calculus:

2-26. Suppose $|\text{grad } g(x)| \neq 0$ at all points x satisfying $g(x) = 0$, then the critical points of $F(x)$ subject to *the constraint* $g(x) = 0$ *are identical with the critical points of the adjusted function* $\tilde{F}(x,\lambda) = F(x) + \lambda g(x)$ *on all of* $\mathbb{R}^{n+1}$. (*The number* λ *is called a Lagrange multiplier.*)

As a simple application of this idea let us return to the problem of invariant directions on spheres mentioned in Section 2-2. Then the following result holds:

EXAMPLE 2-27. *Suppose the mapping* $f\colon S^n \to \mathbb{R}^{n+1}$ *is a gradient system and* $f(x) \neq 0$ *for any* $x \in S^n$. *Then* f *always possesses at least two invariant directions on* S^n.

Proof. Suppose $\operatorname{grad} F(x) = f$ and $F(0) = 0$. Then f possesses an invariant direction provided the equation $f(x) = \lambda x$ has a solution x_0 with $x_0 \in S^n$ and $\lambda \neq 0$. Equivalently, by the above result, we can consider the critical points of $F(x)$ on the sphere $|x| = 1$. As $|x| = 1$ is compact, $F(x)$ always possesses a maximum and a minimum on S^n, and these are invariant directions on S^n. Note that $f(x) \neq 0$ on S^n guarantees $\lambda \neq 0$. ||

Exercises

2-11. Determine the nature of the critical points of $f(x_1,x_2) = 2x_1^4 + x_2^4 - x_1^2 - 2x_2^2$. What is the relation of these critical points to the results of (2-24) and (2-25) in the text above?

2-12. Prove that $a = \inf_{[C]} \max_C F(x)$ of 2-25 is not a relative minimum.

2-13. Suppose both $F(x)$ and $F(x)/|x| \to \infty$ as $|x| \to \infty$. Prove $\text{grad } F = p$ has a solution for every $p \in \mathbb{R}^n$.

2-14. Suppose that $\mathcal{L}(x_1,\ldots,x_{n+1}) = A(x_1,\ldots,x_n)\cdot x_{n+1}$ is a continuous real-valued multilinear function defined on $\Pi_{i=1}^{n+1} \mathbb{R}^n$ symmetric under all permutations of its arguments. Prove $A(x ,\ldots,x) = Ax$ is a gradient operator, and find the real-valued function $B(x)$ such that

$$\text{grad } B = A .$$

2-15. Suppose $F(x)$ is a real-valued continuously differentiable function defined for $x \in \mathbb{R}^n$, and satisfying

(i) $F(x) \to \infty$ as $|x| \to \infty$

(ii) $[\text{grad } F(x) - \text{grad } F(y)] \cdot (x - y) \geq 0$

Prove that $F_c = \{x | F(x) \leq c\}$ is a closed, bounded, convex set in $\mathbb{R}^n$.

§2-4. GRADIENT SYSTEMS WITH NONDEGENERATE CRITICAL POINTS

A gradient system, grad F, in $\mathbb{R}^n$ is <u>nondegenerate</u> if at all critical points of F in $\mathbb{R}^n$, $\det(F_{x_i x_j}) \neq 0$; the matrix $(F_{x_i x_j})$ is called the Hessian of F. An immediate consequence of this definition is that the critical points of $F(x)$ are isolated. Indeed the Jacobian at all solutions of the system $F_{x_i} = 0$ is the Hessian of F, and as the determinant of this matrix is nonzero, the result follows from the

Implicit Function Theorem. A few further introductory remarks are in order:

LEMMA 2-28. <u>The notion of a nondegenerate gradient system is preserved under coordinate transformations.</u>

<u>Proof</u>. If the solutions of $F_{x_i} = 0$ are $x = \bar{x}_\lambda$ and $g: (x_1,\ldots,x_n) \to (g_1,\ldots,g_n)$ is a smooth one-one coordinate transformation, then by 2-21 of the previous section, the new critical points of F occur at $g(\bar{x}_\lambda)$. As in the proof of Lemma 2-21, at a critical point

$$F_{g_i g_k} = \sum_{j,m} (\partial g_k/\partial x_m)^{-1}(\partial g_i/\partial x_j)^{-1} F_{x_m x_j}$$

Thus if the determinant of the Hessian of F vanishes in a given system it vanishes also in any transformed coordinate system. $\|$

LEMMA 2-29. <u>The nondegenerate gradient systems form an open dense set in the class of all</u> C^2 <u>real-valued functions defined on a given compact set</u> M.

<u>Proof</u>. For any given $F(x)$ there is a sequence $\epsilon_N \to 0$ such that (i) if $F_{\epsilon_N} = F(x) + \Sigma\epsilon_{iN}x_i$, then $\max_M \{|F(x) - F_{\epsilon_N}(x)| + |\text{grad } F - \text{grad } F_{\epsilon_N}|\} \to 0$ as $N \to \infty$ and (ii) grad $F_{\epsilon_N}(x)$ is

a nondegenerate gradient system (this is a consequence of Lemma 2-1. Moreover, if $F(x)$ has nondegenerate critical points so does $\tilde{F}(x) = F(x) + G(x)$ provided, $|\text{grad } G|$ and $|G_{x_i x_j}|$ $(i,j = 1,\ldots,n)$ are sufficiently small. Indeed let $\min_M [|\text{grad } F| + |\det(F_{x_i x_j})|] = \mu$, and $|\text{grad } G| < (1/2)\mu$ and $|\det(G_{x_i x_j})| < (1/2)\mu$, then $|\text{grad } \tilde{F}| + |\det(F_{x_i x_j})| > \mu - (1/2)\mu - (1/2)\mu = 0$. ||

LEMMA 2-30. (Morse) <u>Let</u> F <u>be a real-valued</u> C^2 <u>function on</u> $\mathbb{R}^n$. <u>Then at any nondegenerate critical point</u> x_0 <u>there is a coordinate system centered at</u> x_0 <u>in which</u> $F(x) = \Sigma_{i=1}^n \epsilon_i y_i^2$ <u>where</u> $\epsilon_i = \pm 1$ <u>and</u> $\epsilon_{i-1} \leq \epsilon_i$.

<u>Proof</u>. By Lemma 2-22 of Section 2-3,

$$F(x) = \sum_{i=1}^{n} x_i \int_0^1 F_{x_i}(tx)\, dt$$

As $\text{grad } F(x_0) = 0$, integration by parts yields

$$F(x) = \sum_{i,j=1}^{n} x_i x_j \int_0^1 (1 - t) F_{x_i x_j}(tx)\, dt = \sum_{i,j=1}^{n} a_{ij}(x) x_i x_j$$

Case I. If some $a_{ii}(x_0) \neq 0$, which we may suppose to be a_{11}, setting $z_1 = \Sigma_{j=1}^n a_{ij}(x)|a_{11}(x)|^{-1/2} x_j$ and leaving the other variables unchanged by setting $z_i = x_i$, $i \neq 1$, we obtain $F(x) = \pm z_1^2 + Q(z_2,\ldots,z_n)$ where Q is a quadratic form in $z_2,\ldots,z_n$. This change of variables is admissible as $\det(\partial z_j/\partial x_i) \neq 0$ at x_0.

Case II. If all $a_{ii}(x_0) = 0$, as x_0 is a nondegenerate critical point, some $a_{ij}(x_0) \neq 0$, which we suppose to be a_{12}. Then the introduction of new coordinates $x_1 = u_1 - u_2$, $x_2 = u_1 + u_2$, $x_i = u_i$ $(i > 2)$ returns us to Case I. The proof is then completed by a finite repetition of the above process. One checks at each stage that the coordinate transformation is admissible, that is $\det(\partial \tilde{z}_j/\partial x_i) \neq 0$. ||

The <u>index</u> λ of a nondegenerate critical point x_0 is the number of negative ϵ_i in the representation by the above lemma. This integer is independent of the particular transformation used in the transformation of coordinates from (x) to (y) because the linear approximation to the transformation changes $\Sigma_{i,j}\, a_{ij}(x_0)x_ix_j$ to $\Sigma_{i=1}^n\, \epsilon_i y_i^2$ and thus the integer coincides with the index of the quadratic form $\Sigma\, a_{ij}(x_0)x_ix_j$. This integer λ is also related to the index $i(\text{grad } F, x_0)$ defined in Section 2-2 as the algebraic number of solutions of $\text{grad } F(x) = 0$ at x_0. Namely, $i(\text{grad } F, x_0) = (-1)^\lambda$ (see Exercise 2-19). Thus the critical points of a nondegenerate function defined on $\mathbb{R}^n$ can be classified according to their index, that is, there are $(n + 1)$ different types of nondegenerate critical points in $\mathbb{R}^n$ exactly as there are 3 types of nondegenerate critical points in $\mathbb{R}^2$.

Note that a maximum is of type n and a minimum is of type 0; and there are $(n - 1)$ different types of saddle points. By a <u>critical value</u> c of $F(x)$ we shall mean a real number c such that $F^{-1}(c)$ contains a critical point of F. The next lemma shows that, under certain conditions, the critical values of different critical points are distinct.

LEMMA 2-31. *Let* $F(x)$ *be a* C^2 *function with nondegenerate critical points defined on a compact differentiable manifold* $\mathfrak{M}$ *in* $\mathbb{R}^n$. *Then there is a function* $\tilde{F}(x)$ *on* $\mathfrak{M}$ *with nondegenerate critical points such that* $\tilde{F}(x) \neq \tilde{F}(y)$ *for any pair of its critical points* x, y; *and* $\tilde{F}(x)$ *has the same number of critical points of index* λ *as* $F(x)$ *has.*

Proof. As there are only a finite number of critical points on $\mathfrak{M}$, it suffices to proceed inductively. Furthermore, it is sufficient to consider the result locally. Let $F(x)$ be a function defined on a neighborhood of 0 in $\mathbb{R}^n$ with only one nondegenerate critical point at $(0,0,\ldots,0)$. Then there exists a function $\tilde{F}$ with the same domain such that for ϵ, δ arbitrary small positive numbers

(i) $|\tilde{F}(x) - F(x)| \leq \epsilon$ everywhere and $\tilde{F}(x) = F(x)$ outside a neighborhood of $(0,\ldots,0)$

(ii) $\tilde{F}(x)$ has only one nondegenerate critical point

$x_0 = (0,\ldots,0)$

(iii) $\tilde{F}(0) = F(0) + \epsilon$

Set $A = \{x \mid |x| \leq \delta\}$, $B = \{x \mid \delta \leq |x| \leq 2\delta\}$, $C = \{x \mid |x| \geq 2\delta\}$, and let $g(x)\colon \mathbb{R}^n \to [0,1]$ be a C^2 function which is identically 0 on C and 1 on A. Then $\tilde{F}(x) = F(x) + \epsilon g(x)$ fulfills (i) - (iii) provided ϵ is sufficiently small. We check that $F(x)$ has no critical points on B. Indeed on B there are uniform bounds; $|\text{grad } F(x)| \geq \alpha > 0$ and $|\text{grad } g(x)| \leq \beta$. Thus $|\text{grad } \tilde{F}(x)| \geq |\text{grad } F(x)| - \epsilon|\text{grad } g(x)| \geq \alpha - \epsilon\beta$. Hence if ϵ is sufficiently small $\tilde{F}(x)$ has no critical points on B. As there are only finitely many critical points of F on $\mathfrak{M}$, a finite number of alterations of F yield the desired function $\tilde{F}(x)$. ||

Do critical points of index λ exist for some function $F(x)$? We now give a brief summary of the results of M. Morse in this connection. Following Morse, we consider a compact differentiable n-dimensional manifold $\mathfrak{M}$ in $\mathbb{R}^n$. Surely any real-valued twice continuously differentiable function $F(x)$ defined on $\mathfrak{M}$ has an absolute maximum and absolute minimum on $\mathfrak{M}$. Morse showed that certain geometric properties of $\mathfrak{M}$ can be used to guarantee the existence of critical points of index λ on $\mathfrak{M}$, provided $F(x)$ defines a nondegenerate gradient system. Let $\mathfrak{M}^a = \{x \mid x \in \mathfrak{M}, F(x) \leq a\}$. Then the following two geometric results enable one to distinguish nondegenerate critical points of $F(x)$ on $\mathfrak{M}$. First some terminology: Two sets A and B in the space $\mathfrak{M}$ are isotopic if there exists a continuous mapping $\varphi(t,A)$ of A into B such that for each t, $0 \leq t \leq 1$, $\varphi(t,A)$ is homeomorphic to A, $\varphi(0,A) = A$, $\varphi(1,A) = B$.

THEOREM 2-32. *Suppose* $F^{-1}[a,b]$ *contains no critical points of* $F(x)$, *then* $\mathfrak{M}^a$ *and* $\mathfrak{M}^b$ *are isotopic*.

THEOREM 2-33. *Let* x_0 *be a nondegenerate critical point of index* λ *for* $F(x)$ *with* $F(x_0) = c$. *Suppose that for sufficiently small* $\epsilon > 0$, $F^{-1}[c - \epsilon, c + \epsilon]$ *contains no other critical points*. *Then* $\mathfrak{M}^{c+\epsilon}$ *is diffeomorphic to* $\mathfrak{M}^{c-\epsilon} \cup E^\lambda$, *where* E^λ *is a* λ*-cell of the form* $\{|x| \leq c, x_1^2 + \ldots + x_\lambda^2 \leq c^2, x_{\lambda+1} = \ldots = x_n = 0\}$ *and* $\dot{E}^\lambda = \{|x| = c, x_1^2 + \ldots + x_\lambda^2 = c^2, x_{\lambda+1} = \ldots = x_n = 0\}$, *and* $M^{c-\epsilon} \cap E^\lambda = \dot{E}^\lambda$.

We do not prove these results here but refer the reader to the proofs of Milnor [9]. However the ideas involved are illustrated by the following argument.

Outline of the proof of Theorem 2-32 *for* $\mathfrak{M} = S^{n-1}$. The idea is to define the isotopy $\varphi(t,\mathfrak{M}^a)$ by a motion along the orthogonal trajectories to the level surface $F(x) = a$ on

S^{n-1}. To accomplish this, let h be an arbitrary vector in $\mathbb{R}^n$ and denote by $(\ ,\ )$ the scalar product of vectors in $\mathbb{R}^n$. Then along any solution $x(t)$ of the differential equation

$$x' = h - (x,h)x \tag{2-4}$$

(where " ' " denotes differentiation with respect to t) with initial value $x_0 \in S^{n-1}$, one verifies that

$$(x,x)' = 2(x,x') = 0$$

that is, any solution $x(t)$ with initial value $x_0 \in S^{n-1}$ remains on S^{n-1}. Now we attempt to choose h such that along $x(t)$, $F'(x(t))$ is constant; for convenience we suppose the constant is $b - a$. By equation (2-4), we have

$$\begin{aligned} F'(x(t)) &= (\text{grad } F(x(t)),x') = (\text{grad } F - (x,\text{grad } F)x,h) \\ &= (f(x),h) \qquad (\text{say}) \end{aligned}$$

Thus for $x \in F^{-1}[a,b]$, we denote $h = (b - a)f(x)|f(x)|^{-2}$. Such a definition is valid, because $|f(x)| = |\text{grad } F - (x,\text{grad } F)x| \neq 0$. Indeed if $|f(x)| = 0$ for $x \in F^{-1}[a,b]$, then by (2-26) $F(x)$ would have a critical point $x_0 \in S^{n-1} \cap F^{-1}[a,b]$ contrary to the hypothesis of the theorem. Regarding h as a function of x, we extend $h(x)$ smoothly outside of $F^{-1}[a,b]$ to S^{n-1} so that $h(x)$ vanishes off a small compact neighborhood of $F^{-1}[a,b]$. Now by a standard result from the theory of ordinary differential equations, see [10], the initial value problem (2-4) has a uniquely defined solution $x(t,x_0)$ locally, which depends continuously on the initial value x_0. Furthermore, as the right hand side of equation (2-4) vanishes outside a small neighborhood of $F^{-1}[a,b]$, $x(t,x_0)$ may be extended to exist for all t. Then for fixed $t \in [0,1]$, we define the isotopy $\varphi(t,\mathfrak{M}^a)$ as follows: $\varphi(t,\mathfrak{M}^a) = x(t,\mathfrak{M}^a) = \{x(t,x_0) | x_0 \in \mathfrak{M}^a\}$. Clearly $\varphi(0,\mathfrak{M}^a) = \mathfrak{M}^a$; $\varphi(1,\mathfrak{M}^a) = \mathfrak{M}^b$, because for any $x_0 \in F^{-1}(a)$

$$F(x(1,x_0)) = F(x(0,x_0)) - \int_0^1 F'(x(t,x_0))\, dt$$

$$= a - (b - a) = b$$

Furthermore, for each $t \in [0,1]$, one checks that the set $\varphi(t,\mathfrak{M}^a)$ is homeomorphic to $\mathfrak{M}^a$ (see [9]). ||

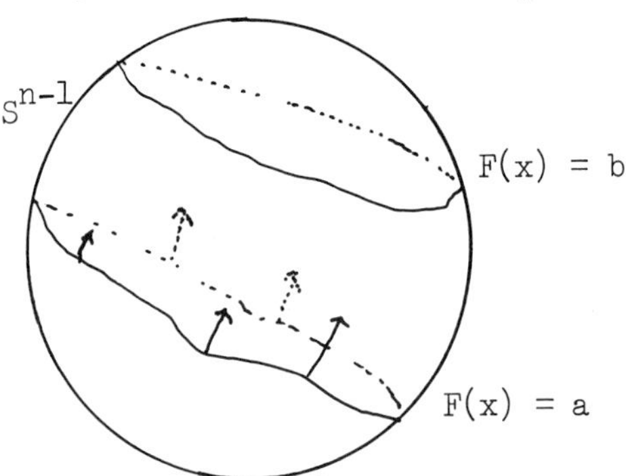

Figure 6. Deforming $\mathfrak{M}^a$ into $\mathfrak{M}^b$ isotopically.

REMARK 2-34. The Theorem 2-33 has a slight generalization to the case in which $F(x)$ has distinct and isolated critical points which are not necessarily nondegenerate. Again if $F^{-1}[c - \epsilon, c + \epsilon]$ contains only the critical point x_0 with $F(x_0) = c$, then $\mathfrak{M}^{c+\epsilon}$ is isotopic to $\mathfrak{M}^{c-\epsilon} \cup E^\beta$ for some β-cell, E^β.

We now show how these results can be used to find lower bounds for the number of critical points of index λ on $\mathfrak{M}$. To this end we suppose we have an integer-valued geometric invariant of pairs of spaces $S_\lambda(X,A)$, $X \supset A$, satisfying the following properties:

(i) Subadditivity for $X \supset Y \supset Z$; that is, $S_\lambda(X,Z) \leq S_\lambda(X,Y) + S_\lambda(Y,Z)$

(ii) Dimension; for a β-cell E^β with boundary $\dot{E}^\beta$, $S_\lambda(E^\beta, \dot{E}^\beta) = \delta_{\lambda\beta}$, the Kronecker delta

(iii) Homotopy invariance; if (X,A) and (Y,B) are of the same homotopy type (see definition in Appendix I) then $S_\lambda(X,A) = S_\lambda(Y,B)$

(iv) Excision; $S_\lambda(X,Y) = S_\lambda(X - U, Y - U)$ for any open set $U \subset \operatorname{int} Y$.

An immediate consequence of these axioms is that (a) $S_\lambda(X_n,X_0) \leq \Sigma_{i=1}^n S_\lambda(X_i,X_{i-1})$ where $X_0 \subset X_1 \subset \dots \subset X_n$ (by induction). Hence (b) if $X_0 = \emptyset$, then $S_\lambda(X_n) \leq \Sigma_{i=1}^n S_\lambda(X_i,X_{i-1})$ where $S_\lambda(X_n)$ denotes $S_\lambda(X_n,\emptyset)$.

Now let $\mathfrak{M}$ be given and let f be a differentiable function on $\mathfrak{M}$ with isolated nondegenerate critical points. Let $\mathfrak{M}^{a_i}$ contain exactly i critical points of f, $a_1 < \dots < a_k$ and $\mathfrak{M}^{a_k} = \mathfrak{M}$, $\emptyset = \mathfrak{M}^{a_0} \subset \dots \subset \mathfrak{M}^{a_k}$.

THEOREM 2-35. _If_ C_λ _denotes the number of critical points of index_ λ _on_ $\mathfrak{M}$, _then_ $S_\lambda(\mathfrak{M}) \leq C_\lambda$.

Proof.
$$\begin{aligned} S_\lambda(\mathfrak{M}) = S_\lambda(\mathfrak{M}^{a_k}) &\leq \sum_{i=1}^{k} S_\lambda(\mathfrak{M}^{a_i}, \mathfrak{M}^{a_{i-1}}) \\ &\leq \sum_{i=1}^{k} S_\lambda(\mathfrak{M}^{a_{i-1}} \cup E^{\lambda_i}, \mathfrak{M}^{a_{i-1}}) && \text{(by (iii))} \\ &\leq \sum_{i=1}^{k} S_\lambda(E^{\lambda_i}, \dot{E}^{\lambda_i}) && \text{(by (iv))} \\ &\leq C_\lambda && \text{(by (ii)).} \end{aligned}$$

The easiest example of such an invariant is the Betti number $R_\lambda(X,A)$ (see Appendix I). It is important to note that by virtue of Lemma 2-31, the above theorem holds even if the critical values a_i of $f(x)$ are not distinct. More precisely, the following result holds.

COROLLARY 2-36. _Let_ $\mathfrak{M}$ _be a compact differentiable manifold and_ $f(x)$ _a real-valued continuously differentiable function defined on_ $\mathfrak{M}$ _having only nondegenerate critical points. Then_ $C_\lambda \geq R_\lambda$ $(\lambda = 0,1,\dots,n)$, _where_ R_λ _are the Betti numbers of_ $\mathfrak{M}$.

Actually more general relations hold between the Betti numbers R_λ $(\lambda = 0,1,\dots,n)$ of a compact differentiable manifold $\mathfrak{M}$ and the number of critical points of a nondegenerate gradient system. These relations are called Morse inequalities and can be written as follows:

$$C_0 \geq R_0$$

$$C_1 - C_0 \geq R_1 - R_0$$

$$C_2 - C_1 + C_0 \geq R_2 - R_1 + R_0$$

$$\dots$$

$$C_\lambda - C_{\lambda-1} + \dots \pm C_0 \geq R_\lambda - R_{\lambda-1} + \dots \pm R_0 \quad (0 \leq \lambda \leq n-1)$$

$$C_n - C_{n-1} + \dots \pm C_0 = R_n - R_{n-1} + \dots \pm R_0$$

We note that the last relation is actually an equation. Its proof is outlined in the problems below. These Morse inequalities are proved in the monograph [9], by utilizing the exactness axiom of homology (see Appendix I) in addition to the properties of the Betti numbers R_λ mentioned above.

Exercises

2-16. Suppose that (x_0,y_0) is a nondegenerate critical point of the harmonic function $u(x,y)$. Prove (x_0,y_0) has index 1.

2-17. Let $f(z_1,z_2,\dots,z_n) = u(x_1,y_1,\dots,x_n,y_n) + iv(x_1,y_1,\dots,x_n,y_n)$ be a continuously differentiable mapping of

$\mathbb{R}^{2n} \to \mathbb{R}^2$, where $z_j = x_j + iy_j$, $i^2 = -1$ and f satisfies the Cauchy-Riemann equations $\partial u/\partial x_j = \partial v/\partial y_j$, and $\partial u/\partial y_j = -\partial v/\partial x_j$ for $j = 1,\ldots,n$. Prove that any nondegenerate critical point of $u(x_1,y_1,\ldots,x_n,y_n)$ has index n.

2-18. Let $\mathfrak{M}$ be a compact differentiable manifold with Betti numbers $R_\lambda(\mathfrak{M})$ $(\lambda = 0,1,\ldots,n)$. Suppose $f(x)$ is a C^2 real-valued function defined on $\mathfrak{M}$ possessing nondegenerate critical points. Derive a lower bound for the number of critical points of $f(x)$ on $\mathfrak{M}$. Show, by example, that if $f(x)$ has degenerate critical points then this lower bound may be violated. (See E. Pitcher, "Inequalities of critical point theory." Bull. Amer. Math. Soc., 64 (1958), 1-30.)

2-19. Suppose $f(x)$ is a smooth real-valued function defined on a compact differentiable manifold $\mathfrak{M}$. Then prove the following relationship between the index $i(\text{grad } f,x_0)$ of grad f at a critical point x_0 of $f(x)$ on $\mathfrak{M}$, defined in Section 2-1 and the index λ at x_0 defined in the above section:

$$i(\text{grad } f,x_0) = (-1)^\lambda$$

2-20. An integer-valued geometric invariant $S(X,A)$ is called additive if for $X \supset Y \supset Z$

$$S(X,Z) = S(X,Y) + S(Y,Z)$$

Prove that if $S(X,A)$ is additive and satisfies

$$\text{(ii)}' \quad S(E^\beta,\dot{E}^\beta) = (-1)^{n+\beta}$$

for any β-cell E^β with boundary $\dot{E}^\beta$, and hypotheses (iii) and (iv) above, then Theorem 2-35 can be extended to prove

$$S(\mathfrak{M}) = S(\mathfrak{M},\phi) = \sum_{i=1}^{n} S(E^{\lambda_i},\dot{E}^{\lambda_i})$$

and

$$S(\mathfrak{M}) = C_n - C_{n-1} + C_{n-2} - \cdots \pm C_0$$

2-21. An additive geometric invariant satisfying (ii)', (iii) and (iv) is the Euler-Poincaré characteristic $\chi(\mathfrak{M})$ (see Appendix I). Use Exercises 2-19 and 2-20 above to verify that the sum of the indices of the vector field defined on $\mathfrak{M}$ by the gradient of any nondegenerate C^2 real-valued function equals $\chi(\mathfrak{M})$.

2-22. Let $p = (p_1,\ldots,p_n)$ be a given point in $\mathbb{R}^n$. Suppose that $\mathfrak{M}$ is the manifold in $\mathbb{R}^n$ defined by $h(x_1,\ldots,x_n) = 0$, where h is an infinitely differentiable real-valued function and $|\text{grad } h| \neq 0$ for $x \in \mathfrak{M}$.

(i) Prove that for any point $x \in \mathfrak{M}$, the distance function $d(x - p) = (x - p)\cdot(x - p)$ defined on $\mathfrak{M}$ has as critical points any point x lying on a normal from p to $\mathfrak{M}$.

(ii) Find a geometric criterion to decide which critical points are nondegenerate.

§2-5. CRITICAL POINTS FOR GENERAL GRADIENT SYSTEMS

Is it possible to estimate the number of critical points on a manifold $\mathfrak{M}$ of a real-valued function $F(x)$ independent of any nondegeneracy condition? We intend to show that such bounds may be achieved, as was first demonstrated by L. Ljusternik and L. Schnirelmann in 1930.

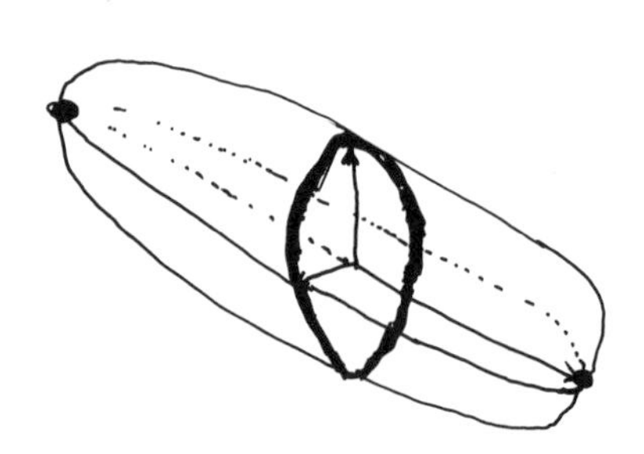

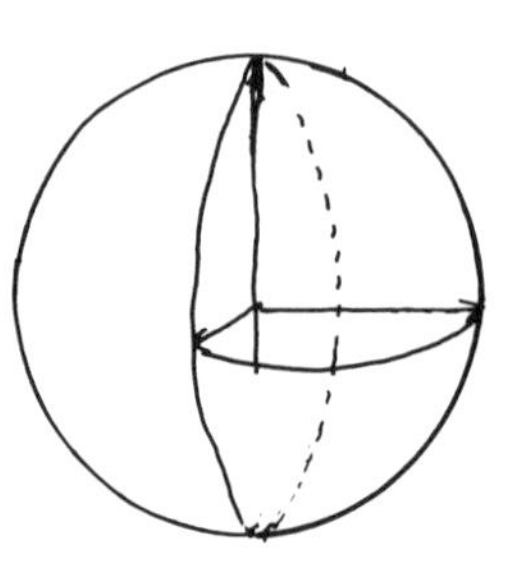

Figure 7. The critical points on $a^2x^2 + b^2y^2 + c^2z^2 = 1$ of $F(x,y,z) = \sqrt{x^2 + y^2 + z^2}$ $(a,b,c \neq 0)$ are degenerate if any two of a,b,c are equal.

First we suppose that the critical points of $F(x)$ are isolated on $\mathfrak{M}$ and that we have an integer-valued geometric invariant $n(A,\mathfrak{M})$ defined on compact sets $A \subset \mathfrak{M}$ satisfying the following properties:

(1) $n(E^\lambda,\mathfrak{M}) = 1$, where E^λ is a cell of any dimension λ on $\mathfrak{M}$ and $n(\phi,\mathfrak{M}) = 0$, where ϕ denotes the empty set

(2) $n(A,\mathfrak{M})$ is an isotopy invariant

(3) $n(A \cup B,\mathfrak{M}) \leq n(A,\mathfrak{M}) + n(B,\mathfrak{M})$; we set $n(\mathfrak{M},\mathfrak{M}) = n(\mathfrak{M})$

The trivial example of such an invariant is obtained by setting $n(A,\mathfrak{M}) = 1$ if $A \neq \phi$, and $n(A,\mathfrak{M}) = 0$ otherwise. An interesting property of such an invariant is contained in the next result.

THEOREM 2-37. *Suppose that* $n(A,\mathfrak{M})$ *satisfies the above properties* (1) - (3). *Then the number of distinct critical points of a continuously differentiable real-valued function*

$F(x)$ <u>on</u> $\mathfrak{M}$ <u>is at least</u> $n(\mathfrak{M})$.

<u>Proof</u>. By the proof of Lemma 2-31 of Section 2-4, we may suppose for any two isolated critical points x and y that $F(x) \neq F(y)$. Thus suppose $\mathfrak{M} = \mathfrak{M}^{a_k} \supset \mathfrak{M}^{a_{k-1}} \supset \ldots \supset \mathfrak{M}^{a_0} = \phi$ where $\mathfrak{M}^{a_i} = \{x \mid x \in \mathfrak{M}, F(x) \leq a_i\}$ and each $\mathfrak{M}^{a_i}$ contains exactly i critical points $\{x_1,\ldots,x_i\}$ so that there are k distinct critical points in all. Then denoting by E^i a sufficiently small neighborhood of x_i,

$$\begin{aligned}
n(\mathfrak{M}) &= \sum_{i=1}^{k} \{n(\mathfrak{M}^{a_i}) - n(\mathfrak{M}^{a_{i-1}})\} \\
&= \sum_{i=1}^{k} \{n(\mathfrak{M}^{a_{i-1}} \cup E^i) - n(\mathfrak{M}^{a_{i-1}})\} && \text{(by (2-34))} \\
&\leq \sum_{i=1}^{k} \{n(\mathfrak{M}^{a_{i-1}}) + n(E^i) - n(\mathfrak{M}^{a_{i-1}})\} && \text{(by (3) above)} \\
&\leq \sum_{i=1}^{k} n(E^i) = k && \text{(by (1) above)}
\end{aligned}$$

To find such an invariant $n(A,\mathfrak{M})$ we generalize the idea of dimension. Let A be a compact subset of $\mathfrak{M}$ and consider coverings of A by compact sets Σ_i each of which is contractible to a point in $\mathfrak{M}$, that is there is a homotopy $H(x,t)\colon \Sigma_i \times [0,1] \to \mathfrak{M}$ such that $H(x,0) = x$ and $H(x,1) = p$ for some fixed $p \in \mathfrak{M}$. We set $\operatorname{cat}(A,\mathfrak{M})$ to be the minimal number of sets in such a covering. If no such finite covering exists, we set $\text{cat}(A,\mathfrak{M}) = \infty$. (We denote $\text{cat}(\mathfrak{M},\mathfrak{M}) = \text{cat}(\mathfrak{M})$, and in fact $\text{cat}(\mathfrak{M}) \leq \dim \mathfrak{M} + 1$ [12].)

LEMMA 2-38. $\text{Cat}(A,\mathfrak{M})$ _satisfies the properties_ (1) - (3).

Proof. Properties (1) and (3) are immediate. To obtain property (2) we let h_t be an isotopy of $A \times [0,1] \to \mathfrak{M}$. It is sufficient to prove that $\text{cat}(A,\mathfrak{M}) \leq \text{cat}(h_1(A),\mathfrak{M})$. Let $h_1(A) \subseteq B_1 \cup \dots \cup B_k$ where each B_i is compact and contractible in $\mathfrak{M}$. If $A_i = h_1^{-1}(B_i \cap h_1(A))$, then A_i is compact in $\mathfrak{M}$. Also $A = A_1 \cup \dots \cup A_k$. Furthermore, A_i is contractible in $\mathfrak{M}$ because h_t continuously deforms A_i into a subset of B_i and B_i is contractible. ||

We now consider the minimax principle of Ljusternik-Schnirelmann for the construction of critical values of real-valued differentiable functions.

MINIMAX THEOREM 2-39. _Suppose_ $F(x)$ _is a real-valued twice continuously differentiable function defined on a compact manifold_ $\mathfrak{M}$ _with isolated critical points_. _Let_ i _be a fixed integer and define_ $[A]_i = \{A \mid n(A,\mathfrak{M}) \geq i\}$ _where_ $n(A,\mathfrak{M})$ _is any invariant satisfying properties_ (1) - (3). _Then provided_ $[A]_i$ _is not vacuous_, $\inf_{[A]_i} \max_A F(x)$ _is achieved and is a critical value of_ F.

Proof. By virtue of the proof of Lemma 2-31 of Section 2-4, we may assume $F(x) \neq F(y)$ for any two critical points x,y. Let $c = \inf_{[A]_i} \max_A F(x)$; the compactness of $\mathfrak{M}$ insures that c is finite and is achieved on $\mathfrak{M}$. Suppose $F^{-1}(c) \cap \mathfrak{M}$ has no critical points. Then by Theorem 2-32, we may find an $\epsilon > 0$ sufficiently small and isotopically deform $\mathfrak{M}^{c+\epsilon}$ into $\mathfrak{M}^{c-\epsilon}$ because $F^{-1}[c - \epsilon, c + \epsilon]$ is compact and has no critical points. Thus every $A \in [A]_i$ with $A \subseteq \mathfrak{M}^{c+\epsilon}$ is moved isotopically to a new set $A' \subseteq \mathfrak{M}^{c-\epsilon}$. Since $[A]_i$ is invariant under isotopy $A' \in [A]_i$ and $\max_{A'} F \leq c - \epsilon$, hence $c = \inf_{[A]_i} \max_A F(x) \leq \max_{A'} F(x) \leq c - \epsilon$, a contradiction. ||

Thus in order to apply the results of this section to concrete problems it is important to find sets $\mathfrak{M}$ with the property that $\operatorname{cat}(\mathfrak{M})$ is large. One space with these properties is real n-dimensional projective space P^n. P^n can be obtained by identifying antipodal points on the sphere S^n. Alternatively, P^n can be obtained from the n-cell Σ_n, that is, $\{x \mid |x| \leq 1, x \in \mathbb{R}^n\}$, by identifying antipodal points on the boundary of Σ_n, namely on S^{n-1}.

LEMMA 2-40. $\operatorname{Cat}(P^n) \leq n + 1$.

Proof. To accomplish this we construct a covering of P^n by

$(n + 1)$ closed, contractible sets in P^n. Such a covering can be constructed, because S^{n-1} can be covered by $(n + 1)$ closed sets $\{A_i\}$ such that $A_i \cap -A_i = \emptyset$, where $-A_i$ is the antipodal image of the set $A_i \subset S^{n-1}$; (a fact which we shall assume for the moment). Then letting f be the identification mapping of antipodal points of S^{n-1}, 0 the center of Σ_n, and $\overline{0A_i}$ the convex join of 0 and A_i; then the sets $f(\overline{0A_i})$ $(i = 1,\ldots,n + 1)$ form a covering of P^n by $(n + 1)$ closed sets each contractible to a point in P^n.

Finally we prove that S^{n-1} has the covering assumed above. The proof proceeds by induction. The case $N = 1$ is clear as 3 closed arcs of 120 degrees each cover S^1. We assume the result holds for $N = n - 2$. Now $S^{n-1} = B^+ \cup B^-$ where $B^+ = \{x|\Sigma_{i=1}^n x_i^2 = 1, x_n \geq -1/2\}$ and $B^- = \{x|\Sigma_{i=1}^n x_i^2 = 1, x_n \leq -1/2\}$. If we set $A_1 = B^-$, it suffices to prove that B^+ can be covered with n closed sets $A_2,\ldots,A_{n+1}$ such that $A_i \cap -A_i = \emptyset$. If we denote by $B_0 = \{x|x \in S^{n-1}, x_n = 0\}$, then B_0 is an equator of S^{n-1} and, by the induction hypothesis, can be covered by n closed sets $\tilde{A}_i \in B_0$ such that $\tilde{A}_i \cap -\tilde{A}_i = \emptyset$. For each $a_i \in \tilde{A}_i$ consider great circle arcs α_i joining a_i to the North Pole $(0,\ldots,0,1)$ and the South Pole $(0,\ldots,0,-1)$. Then we set $A_i = \{x|x \in \alpha_i \cap B^+\}$.

The sets A_i so constructed satisfy $A_i \cap -A_i = \emptyset$. For suppose that x and x^* are an antipodal pair lying in the same A_i, say A_1. Let a_1 and $a_1{}^*$ be the points in $\tilde{A}_1$ generating x and x^* respectively, in our construction. Clearly $a_1 \neq a_1{}^*$ but a_1 and $a_1{}^*$ both lie on the equator and on a great circle passing through the North Pole. Hence $a_1 = -a_1{}^*$ contradicting the fact that $\tilde{A}_1 \cap -\tilde{A}_1 = \phi$. ||

THEOREM 2-41. $\mathrm{Cat}(P^n) = n + 1$.

Proof. Perhaps the most informative method of deducing the fact that $\mathrm{cat}(P^n) \geq n + 1$, is via the multiplicative structure of the homology of P^n (cf. Hilton-Wylie [11]). However an equivalent result on coverings of spheres can be proved by the methods we have studied so far. We shall show that if S^{n-1} is covered by p closed sets A_i such that $A_i \cap -A_i = \phi$ $(i = 1,\ldots,p)$, then $p \geq n + 1$. (This signifies that $\mathrm{cat}(P^n) \geq n + 1$ provided we restrict coverings of P^n to those of the form $\{f(\overline{OA_i}) \mid i = 1,\ldots,p\}$, as in the above paragraph.) Without loss of generality to obtain a contradiction we may suppose $p = n$ (if $p < n$, we merely add $n - p$ points of S^n to the covering). In this case, we define a sequence of real-valued functions

$$\zeta_i(x) = \begin{cases} 1 & \text{if } x \in A_i \\ -1 & \text{if } x \in -A_i \end{cases} \tag{2-5}$$

for $(i = 1,\ldots,n)$. By virtue of the Tietze Extension Theorem, we can extend each ζ_i to a continuous mapping of $S^{n-1} \to \mathbb{R}^1$. Then the vector-valued mapping $\zeta(x) = (\zeta_1(x),\ldots,\zeta_n(x))$ is continuous from $S^{n-1} \to \mathbb{R}^n$, and has the property that $\zeta(x) \neq 0$ for $x \in S^{n-1}$. Indeed $x \in A_i$ for some i and thus by (2-5) $\zeta(x) \neq 0$. Thus $\tilde{\zeta}(x) = \zeta(x)/|\zeta(x)|$ is a continuous mapping of S^{n-1} into itself. We obtain a contradiction by showing: (a) $\tilde{\zeta}(S^{n-1}) = S^{n-1}$ and (b) $\tilde{\zeta}(S^{n-1})$ omits the point $(1,0,\ldots,0)$.

The demonstration of (a) is based on the Borsuk-Ulam Theorem 2-17. For if $\tilde{\zeta}(S^{n-1})$ omits a point p of S^{n-1} we may define a continuous mapping $\tilde{\tilde{\zeta}}: S^{n-1} \to \mathbb{R}^{n-1}$ by setting $\tilde{\tilde{\zeta}} = \pi\tilde{\zeta}$ where π is the stereographic projection with the point p as North Pole. Thus by the Borsuk-Ulam Theorem, there is a point $x_0 \in S^{n-1}$ such that $\tilde{\tilde{\zeta}}(x_0) = \tilde{\tilde{\zeta}}(-x_0)$. This equation however implies $\tilde{\zeta}(x_0) = \tilde{\zeta}(-x_0)$, that is, $\zeta_i(x_0) = \zeta_i(-x_0)$ for $(i = 1,\ldots,n)$ which is not possible as $x_0 \in A_j$ for some j and by (2-5) above $\zeta_j(x_0) \neq \zeta_j(-x_0)$.

The demonstration of (b) also proceeds by contradiction. Suppose that $\tilde{\zeta}(x_1) = (1,0,\ldots,0)$. Then $x_1 \in A_1$ and $-x_1 \in A_k$ with $k \neq 1$, so by (2-5), $\tilde{\zeta}(x_1) \neq (1,0,\ldots,0)$ as the k-th coordinate of $\tilde{\zeta}(x_1)$ is nonzero. ||

A real nonsingular symmetric $n \times n$ matrix A has n real eigenvalues $\lambda_1,\lambda_2,\ldots,\lambda_n$ and at least n eigenvectors on the sphere $|x| = 1$. We now study how this result may be extended to a nonlinear context. We consider the problem of invariant directions, or the solution of the equation $Ax = \lambda x$, on $|x| = 1$ and its reformulation in terms of the critical points of the real-valued function $(1/2)x \cdot Ax$ on $|x| = 1$ mentioned in the Section 2-3. Then the following result holds.

EXAMPLE 2-42. _Suppose_ $f(x): S^{n-1} \to \mathbb{R}^n$ _is a continuously differentiable gradient system, satisfying the conditions_ $f(-x) = -f(x)$ _and_ $f(x) \neq 0$ _for_ $x \in S^{n-1}$. _Then the equation_ $f(x) = \lambda x$ _has at least_ $2n$ _distinct solutions_ $\{x_i\}$ $(i = 1,\ldots,2n)$ _on_ S^{n-1}.

Proof. $F(x) = \int_0^1 f(tx) \cdot x \, dt$ is a real-valued C^2 function whose gradient is f. Furthermore $f(-x) = -f(x)$ implies $F(-x) = F(x)$. Thus if we identify antipodal points of the sphere S^{n-1} to obtain P^{n-1}, $F(x)$ may be regarded as a real-valued function given on P^{n-1}. Thus by Theorem 2-41 and the remarks just above, such a function has at least n critical points $\{x_i\}$ $(i = 1,\ldots,n)$ on P^{n-1}. Hence there are twice as may critical points on S^{n-1}, namely x_i and $-x_i$ $(i = 1,\ldots,n)$. ||

Exercises

2-23. A torus T^2 can be defined as the Cartesian product $S^1 \times S^1$. Let $f(x)$ be a twice continuously differentiable function defined on T^2. How many critical points of $f(x)$ must exist on T^2 if

(i) $f(x)$ has only nondegenerate critical points?

(ii) $f(x)$ may have degenerate critical points?

(Hint: $R_0(T^2) = R_2(T^2) = 1$, $R_1(T^2) = 2$, and $\text{cat}(S^1 \times S^1) = \text{cat}(S^1) + \text{cat}(S^1) - 1$.)

2-24. An n-dimensional torus T^n is defined in $\mathbb{R}^{2n}$ by the system of equations $x_i^2 + y_i^2 = 1$ $(i = 1,\ldots,n)$. Let $F(x_1,y_1,\ldots,x_n,y_n)$ be a three times continuously differentiable function defined on T^n. Assuming that $\text{cat}(T^n) = n + 1$, prove that the system $F_{x_i}y_i - F_{y_i}x_i = 0$ $(i = 1, \ldots,n)$ has at least $(n + 1)$ real solutions on T^n. (Hint: set $V(x,y,\lambda) = F(x_1,y_1,\ldots,x_n,y_n) - \Sigma_{i=1}^n (x_i^2 + y_i^2)\lambda_i$. Then at a critical point,

$$F_{x_i} - 2\lambda_i x_i = 0, \quad F_{y_i} - 2\lambda_i y_i = 0, \quad x_i^2 + y_i^2 = 1.)$$

2-25. Let m_i $(i = 1,\ldots,n)$ be a system of particles, each of which is constrained to lie on a smooth manifold $\mathfrak{M}_i$, homeomorphic to the sphere S^2. Suppose the particles interact by means of a force that is the gradient of a smooth potential function $V(x)$. Prove that the system of particles has at least $(n + 1)$ equilibrium positions. (Hint: Equilibrium points are critical points of $V(x)$ on $\mathfrak{M} = \Pi_{i=1}^n \mathfrak{M}_i$. Furthermore, $\text{cat}(\mathfrak{M}) = n + 1$.)

2-26. Use the fact that $\text{cat}(P^n) = n + 1$ to prove the Borsuk-Ulam Theorem.

2-27. The eigenvalues λ_i $(i = 1,\ldots,n)$ of a positive definite self-adjoint matrix A (arranged in decreasing order and counted according to multiplicity) can be characterized as follows:

$$\lambda_i^{-1} = \inf_{[T]_i} \max_T (Ax,x)$$

where T is the subset of elements of length 1 of some i-dimensional linear subspace $\mathfrak{T}$ in $\mathbb{R}^n$, and $[T]_i$ is the class of all such subsets for fixed integral i as $\mathfrak{T}$ varies. Deduce a similar result from the Minimax Theorem 2-39 of the above section, under the assumption that all the eigenvalues λ_i have multiplicity 1. Can this result be obtained by Corollary 2-36 of the preceding section on non-degenerate gradient systems? (Hint: $\text{cat}(P^m,P^n) = m + 1$ for integral $m \leq n$.)

2-28. Prove the following important extension of the Minimax Theorem 2-39. Let $c_i = \inf_{[A]_i} \max_A F(x)$, then under the hypotheses of Theorem 2-39, if $c = c_i = c_{i+1} = \ldots = c_{i+p}$ $(p > 0)$, then $\text{cat}(K_c,\mathfrak{M}) \geq p + 1$ where $K_c = \{x | x \in \mathfrak{M} \cap F^{-1}(c),$ x a critical point of $F\}$. What does this result imply in case the eigenvalues of the matrix A of Exercise 2-27 are degenerate?

§2-6. SYSTEMS DEFORMABLE TO GRADIENT SYSTEMS

Let $f(x)$ be a continuous mapping of the closure of a bounded domain D containing the origin in $\mathbb{R}^n$ into $\mathbb{R}^n$. We call $f(x)$ a gradient-like system provided there is a continuously differentiable real-valued function $F(x)$ such that $(\text{grad } F(x))\cdot f(x) > 0$ on ∂D.

A simple gradient-like system is obtained by setting

grad $F(x) = x$ if the associated function f satisfies $f(x)\cdot x > 0$. For such systems, $f(x) = 0$ always has solutions; for by the Poincaré-Bohl Theorem 2-9, $d(f,0,D) = d(x,0,D) = 1$, and thus by the property 2-12 of degree $f(x) = 0$ has solutions $x \in D$. More generally the following result holds.

THEOREM 2-43. _Suppose that_ $f(x)$ _is a continuous mapping of_ $\mathbb{R}^n$ _into itself such that_ $(f(x)\cdot x)|x|^{-1} \to \infty$ _as_ $|x| \to \infty$, _then_ $f(x) = p$ _has a solution for every_ $p \in \mathbb{R}^n$.

Proof. $(f(x) - p)\cdot x = f(x)\cdot x - p\cdot x \geq f(x)\cdot x - |p||x| = |x|[(f(x)\cdot x)|x|^{-1} - |p|] > 0$ for sufficiently large $|x|$. Hence $f(x) - p$ is a gradient-like system on sufficiently large spheres. ||

We now obtain a slight generalization of this result.

THEOREM 2-44. _Suppose_ $f(x)$ _is a continuous mapping of_ $\mathbb{R}^n$ _into_ $\mathbb{R}^n$ _and_ $F(x)$ _is a positive real-valued continuously differentiable function defined on_ $\mathbb{R}^n$ _such that_

(1) $(f(x)\cdot\text{grad } F(x))|\text{grad } F(x)|^{-1}$ _and_ $F(x) \to \infty$ _as_ $|x| \to \infty$, _and_

(2) $(\text{grad } F(x) - \text{grad } F(y))\cdot(x - y) > 0$ _for_ $x \neq y$ _with_ $\text{grad } F(0) = 0$.

<u>Then</u> $f(x) = p$ <u>has a solution for every</u> $p \in \mathbb{R}^n$.

<u>Proof</u>. First we note that $f(x) - p$ is a gradient-like system on large spheres Σ_R. Indeed, $|\text{grad } F(x)| \neq 0$ by (2) and

$$\begin{aligned}(f(x) - p)\cdot\text{grad } F(x) &= f(x)\cdot\text{grad } F(x) - p\cdot\text{grad } F(x)\\ &\geq |\text{grad } F(x)|[(f(x)\cdot\text{grad } F(x))|\text{grad } F(x)|^{-1} - |p|]\\ &> 0\end{aligned}$$

Thus by the Poincaré-Bohl Theorem 2-9, $d(f,p,D) = d(\text{grad } F(x),0,D)$ where D is any bounded domain with ∂D outside Σ_R, provided both degrees are defined. $F_c = \{x | F(x) \leq c\}$ for sufficiently large c is a nonempty closed bounded convex set (see Exercise 2-15), and choose $c' > \max_{\Sigma_R} F(x)$. Thus on $\partial F_c = \{x | F(x) = c\}$, grad $F(x)$ defines a nonvanishing vector field directed along the inner or outer normal. Hence $d(\text{grad } F(x),0,F_c) \neq 0$ and so $d(f,p,F_c) \neq 0$ implying that $f(x) = p$ has a solution in F_c. ||

<u>Exercises</u>

2-29. Prove that any real $n \times n$ positive definite matrix is deformable to a gradient system.

2-30. Let A be a nonsingular $n \times n$ matrix, and suppose f is a continuous mapping of $\mathbb{R}^n$ into $\mathbb{R}^n$ such that

$|f(x)||x|^{-1} \to 0$ as $|x| \to \infty$. Show that $Ax + f(x) = p$ has a solution for each $p \in \mathbb{R}^n$ provided that the quadratic form $Ax \cdot x$ is positive definite.

2-31. Let A be a self-adjoint nonsingular matrix, and let $f(x)$ be a continuous mapping of $\mathbb{R}^n \to \mathbb{R}^n$ such that $(f(x)/|x|) \to 0$ uniformly as $|x| \to 0$. Prove

(i) $x - \lambda(Ax + f(x))$ is deformable to a gradient system provided $|x|$ is sufficiently small and λ^{-1} is not an eigenvalue of A.

(ii) the index $i(I - \lambda A, 0)$, where λ^{-1} is not an eigenvalue of A, is ± 1; and determine the index explicitly in terms of λ.

(iii) if all the eigenvalues of A are simple, the equation $x = \lambda(Ax + f(x))$ has at least two distinct solutions for λ^{-1} in a small neighborhood of each eigenvalue of A.

Bibliography

1. B. Malgrange, Ideals of Differentiable Functions, Oxford Univ. Press, London, 1966.

2. J. Hadamard, "Sur quelques applications de l'indice de Kronecker", (Appendix to Tannery: Introduction à la théorie des fonctions d'une variable II, 2. éd. 1910).

3. S. T. Hu, Homotopy Theory, Academic Press, New York, 1959.

4. S. T. Hu, Homology, Holden-Day, San Francisco, 1966.

5. E. Heinz, An elementary analytic theory of degree, Journal Math. Mech. 8 (1959), 231-247.

6. J. Cronin, Fixed Points and Topological Degree in Nonlinear Analysis, Amer. Math. Soc., 1964.

7. J. Milnor, Topology from the Differentiable Viewpoint, University Press of Virginia, Charlottesville, 1965.

8. M. Spivak, Calculus on Manifolds, W. A. Benjamin, New York, 1965.

9. J. Milnor, Morse Theory, Princeton Univ. Press, Princeton, 1963.

10. Coddington and Levinson, Theory of Ordinary Differential Equations, McGraw-Hill, New York, 1955.

11. Hilton and Wylie, Homology Theory, Cambridge Univ. Press, 1960.

12. L. Ljusternik and L. Schnirelmann, Methodes Topologiques dans les Problèmes Variationels, Hermann et Cie., Paris 1934.

CHAPTER 3

INFINITE DIMENSIONAL SYSTEMS

We shall be concerned with operator equations $Ax = p$ where x and p are elements of some infinite dimensional space X. We consider situations in which the qualitative aspects of such systems can be reduced to an analogous finite dimensional system, and for which the methods of Chapter 2 apply. Of particular interest are the many new infinite dimensional phenomena that arise. The chapter begins with a description of the extension of the degree of a mapping from finite to infinite dimensions. Elementary results centered about gradient systems and critical points are also taken up. The chapter ends with a special but important topic concerning the relationship between nonlinear equations and their linearizations.

DEFINITIONS 3-1. A Banach space X over the real numbers is a vector space over the real numbers together with a real-valued function $||x||$ defined for each $x \in X$ and satisfying (a) $||x|| \geq 0$ with equality if and only if $x = 0$; (b) $||x + y|| \leq ||x|| + ||y||$; (c) $||\alpha x|| = |\alpha|\,||x||$; (d) the set X is complete with respect to the metric $d(x,y) = ||x - y||$. Standard examples of infinite dimensional Banach spaces are obtained by fixing a bounded open set Ω in $\mathbb{R}^n$ with closure $\bar{\Omega}$. Then the set of continuous functions defined over $\bar{\Omega}$ is a Banach space, denoted $C(\bar{\Omega})$, provided we choose as norm $||u|| = \max_{\bar{\Omega}} |u(t)|$. Furthermore, for any positive number p, $1 < p < \infty$, the set of functions $u(t)$ whose Lebesgue integral $\int_\Omega |u|^p < \infty$ is a Banach space, denoted $L_p(\Omega)$, where $||u||_{L_p(\Omega)} = (\int_\Omega |u|^p)^{1/p}$. (Functions differing on a set of measure zero are identified.)

<u>A Hilbert space</u> H over the real numbers is a vector space over the real numbers with an inner product (x,y) satisfying (a) (x,y) is a bilinear form on H; (b) H is a Banach space with respect to the norm $||x|| = \sqrt{(x,x)}$. Standard examples of Hilbert spaces are: (1) the set of functions $L_2(\Omega)$ (defined above) with inner product $(u,v) = \int_\Omega u(t)v(t)$ and (2) the space of square summable sequences ℓ_2 with elements $u = (u_1, u_2, \ldots)$ and $v = (v_1, v_2, \ldots)$ and inner product $(u,v) = \Sigma_{i=1}^{\infty} u_i v_i$.

<u>Weak convergence</u> in a Hilbert space H: by $x_n \rightharpoonup y$

weakly we mean $(x_n, z) \to (y, z)$ for all $z \in H$. In contrast, convergence in norm (or strong convergence) of elements $x_n \to y$ in H means $\|x_n - y\| \to 0$. In this regard we note the following facts: (a) weak limits are unique; (b) if $x_n \to y$ weakly in H, then the set of H-norms of the sequence $\{x_n\}$ is uniformly bounded; (c) any sequence in H whose norms are uniformly bounded has a weakly convergent subsequence; (d) if $\|x_n - y\| \to 0$ (that is, $x_n \to y$ strongly), then $x_n \to y$ weakly; but not conversely; (e) in a finite dimensional Hilbert space weak and strong convergence coincide. (For proofs and further discussion see [1].)

§3-1. THE DEGREE OF A CLASS OF OPERATORS IN SPACES OF INFINITE DIMENSION

A new phenomenon arises when one attempts to define the degree of an arbitrary continuous mapping A from one infinite dimensional space X into another such space Y. This fact is clearly seen by means of the following example.

EXAMPLE 3-2. A continuous mapping of the sphere $\|x\| = 1$ of an infinite dimensional space X into itself without a fixed point.

Consider the infinite dimensional Hilbert space ℓ_2,

the space of all square summable real sequences $x = (x_1, x_2, \dots, x_n, \dots)$ with norm $\|x\|^2 = \Sigma_{i=1}^{\infty} x_i^2$. We define an operator T on the set $\Sigma = \{x \mid \|x\| \leq 1\}$ by setting $Tx = (\sqrt{1 - \|x\|^2}, x_1, x_2, \dots)$. T is a continuous mapping as it is the sum of two continuous mappings: $Tx = (\sqrt{1 - \|x\|^2}, 0, 0, \dots) + (0, x_1, x_2, \dots)$. Furthermore T maps the sphere Σ into itself. Indeed if $\|x\| \leq 1$, then $\|Tx\|^2 = 1 - \|x\|^2 + \Sigma_{i=1}^{\infty} x_i^2 = 1$. Assume now that T has a fixed point $\bar{x}$, that is, $T\bar{x} = \bar{x}$, then necessarily $\|\bar{x}\| = 1$. Hence for $T\bar{x} = (0, \bar{x}_1, \bar{x}_2, \dots)$ to equal $\bar{x} = (\bar{x}_1, \bar{x}_2, \dots)$, $\bar{x}_i = 0$ $(i = 1, 2, \dots)$. Thus $\bar{x} = 0$, in contradiction to the fact that $\|\bar{x}\| = 1$. So T has no fixed point in Σ. ||

Thus the direct generalization of the Brouwer Fixed Point Theorem is false: a general continuous mapping of an infinite dimensional space into itself need not have a fixed point. As the proof of the Brouwer Theorem is a consequence of the most elementary properties of the degree of a mapping, such a degree function cannot in general be defined for the operator $(I - T)$, where I is the identity operator $I(x) = x$. A large class of nonlinear operators N for which the Brouwer Fixed Point Theorem is valid and for which the associated degree of the mapping $(I + N)$ can be defined is the class of compact operators. These operators were intensively studied by J. Schauder in the 1920's and are defined as follows.

DEFINITION 3-3. *Let* N *be a mapping of a Banach space* X *into a Banach space* Y. N *is compact provided it is continuous (with respect to convergence in norm) and maps any bounded sequence of* X *into a sequence with a convergent subsequence.*

A basic property of compact operators proven by Schauder is the following:

APPROXIMATION LEMMA 3-4. *Let* N *be a compact operator mapping the Banach space* X *into the Banach space* Y. *Then given* $\epsilon > 0$, *there is a continuous finite dimensional mapping* N_ϵ *with domain contained in* X *and finite dimensional range* $Y_k \subset Y$, *such that* $\|Nx - N_\epsilon x\| \leq \epsilon$ *for every* x *in any given bounded subset* S *of* X.

Proof. As N is a compact mapping, $\overline{N(S)}$ is a compact set in Y. Thus given $\epsilon > 0$, $\overline{N(S)}$ can be covered by a finite number of spheres with centers y_i $(i = 1,\ldots,k)$ and radius ϵ. Let Y_k denote the finite dimensional subspace spanned by $y_1,y_2,\ldots,y_k$. We now construct a partition of unity on S as follows. For every $i = 1,2,\ldots,k$ set

$$\mu_i(x) = \max(0,\epsilon - \|Nx - y_i\| \quad \text{and} \quad \lambda_i(x) = \mu_i(x)[\sum_{i=1}^{k} \mu_i(x)]^{-1}$$

Then the $\mu_i(x)$ are continuous real-valued functions defined on X and as, for $x \in S$ there is some $\mu_i(x) > 0$, $\Sigma_{i=1}^{k} u_i(x) \neq 0$. Thus $\lambda_i(x)$ is a continuous real-valued function defined on S. Furthermore $0 \leq \lambda_i(x) \leq 1$ and $\Sigma_{i=1}^{k} \lambda_i(x) = 1$ for $x \in S$. Now we define an approximation to N for $x \in S$ by setting $N_\epsilon x = \Sigma_{j=1}^{k} \lambda_j(x) y_j$. Then as $Nx = \Sigma_{j=1}^{k} \lambda_j(x) Nx$ for $x \in S$, we have $\|N_\epsilon x - Nx\| = \|\Sigma_{j=1}^{k} \lambda_j(x)[Nx - y_j]\| \leq \Sigma_{j=1}^{k} \lambda_j(x)\|Nx - y_j\| \leq \epsilon$. Furthermore N_ϵ is a continuous function with domain S and range contained in the convex hull of the points $y_1, y_2, \ldots, y_k$ and thus in Y_k. ||

It turns out that the degree of a continuous mapping T of an infinite dimensional Banach space X into itself can be defined as in Section 2-2 provided T can be written $T = I + N$ where I is the identity mapping and N is a compact mapping. Finite dimensional approximations to operators of this form have the following property.

LEMMA 3-5. *Let* $f\colon \bar{D} \to \mathbb{R}^n$ *be a continuous mapping, where* D *is a bounded domain in* $\mathbb{R}^{n+m}$ $(m > 0)$. *Then* $d(x + f(x), p, D) = d(x + f(x), p, D \cap \mathbb{R}^n)$ *for all* $p \in \mathbb{R}^n$ *provided* $x + f(x) \neq p$ *for* $x \in \partial D$.

Proof. It is sufficient to prove the result in case f is a C^1 mapping and the Jacobian determinant in $\mathbb{R}^{n+m}$ of

$x + f(x)$ (which we denote $\det(J_{n+m}(x))$) does not vanish at any solution of $x + f(x) = p$ for $p \in \mathbb{R}^n$ and any $x \in D$, where $f(x) = (f_1(x), f_2(x), \ldots, f_n(x), 0, \ldots, 0)$. In such a case, by the analytic definition of the degree of a mapping

$$\begin{aligned} d(x + f(x), p, D) &= \sum_{x+f(x)=p} \operatorname{sgn} \det(J_{n+m}(x)) \\ &= \sum_{x+f(x)=p} \operatorname{sgn} \det \begin{vmatrix} J_n(x) & 0 \\ 0 & I_m \end{vmatrix} \\ &= \sum_{x+f(x)=p} \operatorname{sgn} \det(J_n(x)) \\ &= d(x + f(x), p, D \cap \mathbb{R}^n) \end{aligned}$$

where I_m is the identity matrix in $\mathbb{R}^m$. ||

Now on to the main result.

THEOREM 3-6. *Suppose* D *is any bounded open subset of a Banach space* X *which meets every finite dimensional subspace of* X *in a bounded open set*. *Let* $Tx = p$ *have no solutions on* ∂D, *where* $T = I + N$ *and* N *is a compact operator defined on* $\bar{D}$. *Then an integer-valued function* $d(T, p, D)$ *can be defined satisfying the properties of Section* 2-2.

Proof. The idea is to compute finite dimensional approximations T_n to the operator T (such that $\|T_n x - Tx\| \to 0$ as $n \to \infty$ uniformly for all $x \in \bar{D}$) and their associated degrees

$d_n = d(T_n, p, D_n)$ where D_n denotes a finite dimensional bounded open set. One then shows that the numbers d_n stabilize for n sufficiently large, that is $d_n = d_{n_0}$ for all $n \geq n_0$.

More precisely, we begin by noting that there is a positive number α such that $\|Tx - p\| > \alpha$ for $x \in \partial D$. For otherwise there would be a bounded sequence $\{x_j\}$ with $\|Tx_j - p\| = \|x_j + Nx_j - p\| \to 0$. By the compactness of N, some subsequence of $\{Nx_j\}$ which we again label $\{x_j\}$ converges to y (say); that is, $\|x_j + y - p\| \to 0$ so that $x_j \to p - y = z$ and $z \in \partial D$ as ∂D is closed. Hence $Tz = p$ for some $z \in \partial D$ contrary to assumption.

Next by the Approximation Lemma 3-4, we may choose a finite dimensional mapping $N_\alpha x$ for Nx such that

$$\|N_\alpha x - Nx\| \leq (1/2)\alpha \quad \text{for} \quad x \in \overline{D} \tag{3-1}$$

Let X_α denote the subspace of X generated by the elements of the range of N_α, and set $\dim X_\alpha = k_\alpha$. By choosing a basis in the vector space X_α we may identify X_α with $\mathbb{R}^k$. Furthermore, let $T_\alpha x = x + N_\alpha x$ and $d_\alpha = d(T_\alpha, p, X_\alpha \cap D)$. Note that d_α is well-defined, as $x + N_\alpha x \neq p$ for $x \in \partial(D \cap X_\alpha)$. Indeed $\|T_\alpha x - p\| = \|Tx - p - Nx + N_\alpha x\| \geq \|Tx - p\| - \|Nx - N_\alpha x\| \geq \alpha - (1/2)\alpha > 0$. We now show that d_α is independent of the particular finite dimensional approximation N_α by showing that (i) d_α is independent of the basis chosen in X_α and (ii) for any two such mappings $N_\alpha^{(1)}$ and $N_\alpha^{(2)}$ satisfying (3-1) their respective degrees satisfy $d_\alpha^{(1)} = d_\alpha^{(2)}$. To verify (i), we remark that if T_α is C^1, the sign of the Jacobian determinant at a point is invariant under a change of basis in X_α. Thus by the analytic definition (i) of degree, (i) follows for C^1 mappings and so for general continuous T_α by taking limits. To verify (ii) suppose $X_\alpha^{(1)}$ and $X_\alpha^{(2)}$ denote the associated approximating subspaces, and let $\tilde{X}_\alpha$ be the subspace of X generated by the elements of $X_\alpha^{(1)}$ and $X_\alpha^{(2)}$. By Lemma 3-5,

$$d(T_\alpha^{(1)}, p, \tilde{X}_\alpha \cap D) = d_\alpha^{(1)} \tag{3-2}$$

and similarly for $T_\alpha^{(2)}$ and $X_\alpha^{(2)}$. Consider the homotopy on $\tilde{X}_\alpha \cap D$ defined by $H(x,t) = t(T_\alpha^{(1)}x - p) + (1 - t)(T_\alpha^{(2)}x - p)$. In the present case on $\tilde{X}_\alpha \cap \partial D = \partial(\tilde{X}_\alpha \cap D)$,

$$\begin{aligned} \|H(x,t)\| &= \|t(Tx - p) + (1 - t)(Tx - p) + H(x,t) - (Tx - p)\| \\ &\geq \|Tx - p\| - t\|T_\alpha^{(1)}x - Tx\| - (1 - t)\|T_\alpha^{(2)}x - Tx\| \\ &> \alpha - (1/2)t\alpha - (1/2)(1 - t)\alpha \\ &> (1/2)\alpha \\ &> 0 \end{aligned}$$

Hence by the homotopy invariance of degree,

$$d(T_\alpha^{(1)}, p, \tilde{X}_\alpha \cap D) = d(T_\alpha^{(2)}, p, \tilde{X}_\alpha \cap D) \qquad (3\text{-}3)$$

Combining (3-2) and (3-3), we obtain $d_\alpha^{(1)} = d_\alpha^{(2)}$. ||

(Note: The class of operators $\{T = I + N | N \text{ is compact}\}$ is by no means the most general class for which the degree of a mapping can be defined. It is however a sufficiently broad class to include the applications discussed here.)

A verification of some of the properties of degree. Here we indicate how the properties of degree are carried over to the infinite dimensional case.

3-7. *If* $d(I + N, p, D) \neq 0$, *then there is an* $x \in D$ *such that* $x + Nx = p$. (*If* $p = 0$, *this is sometimes called the Schauder-Leray Fixed Point Theorem.*)

Proof. Let $\{N_n\}$ be a sequence of mappings with finite dimensional ranges such that $\|N_n x - Nx\| \leq 1/n$ for $x \in \bar{D}$, and let d_n be their associated degrees. Then for sufficiently large n, $d_n \neq 0$ because $d(I + N, p, D) \neq 0$. Hence by the finite dimensional property of degree, there is a point $x_n \in D$ satisfying $x_n + N_n x_n = p$. As N is compact Nx_n has a convergent subsequence which we again label x_n and $\|x_n + Nx_n - p\| \leq \|Nx_n - N_n x_n\| + \|x_n + N_n x_n - p\| \leq 1/n$. Thus as $n \to \infty$, x_n converges to an element x (say) and x satisfies $x + Nx = p$, as required. ||

3-8. (*Homotopy Invariance*) *Suppose* $N(t,x)$ *is a compact mapping of* $[0,1] \times X \to X$. *If* D *is a bounded open set as in Theorem* 3-6 *and* $x + N(t,x) \neq p$ *for* $x \in \partial D$ *and* $t \in [0,1]$, *then* $d(x + N(t,x),p,D)$ *is constant for* $t \in [0,1]$.

Proof. The proof is immediate from the finite dimensional result on homotopy invariance. Indeed the Approximation Lemma 3-4 insures that $N(t,x)$ may be approximated by finite dimensional mappings uniformly, valid for $t \in [0,1]$. ||

3-9. *Schauder Fixed Point Theorem* (*Generalized Brouwer Fixed Point Theorem*) *Let* Σ *be a sphere containing the origin in the Banach space* X, *and* N *a compact mapping of* Σ *into itself*. *Then the equation* $Nx = x$ *has at least one solution*.

Proof. Again we argue as in the finite dimensional case. First note, however, that the operator $tN(x)$ is a compact mapping of $[0,1] \times \Sigma \to \Sigma$. By the homotopy invariance property of degree

$$d(x - tN(x),0,\Sigma) = d(x,0,\Sigma) = 1$$

provided $x - tN(x) \neq 0$ on $\partial\Sigma$ where $t \in [0,1]$. In either case, $Nx = x$ has at least one solution; for if $x - N(x) \neq 0$ on $\partial\Sigma$, then $d(x - N(x),0,\Sigma) = 1$. ||

Exercises

3-1. Prove that a compact mapping N of a closed bounded convex set K in a Banach space X into itself has a fixed point.

3-2. Let L be a linear compact mapping of a Banach space X into itself with $(Lu,u) > 0$, $u \neq 0$. Prove (i) $d(x - \lambda Lx, 0, D)$ is defined provided λ^{-1} is not an eigenvalue of L, (ii) $d(I - \lambda L, 0, D) = (-1)^{\beta}$ where β is the number of eigenvalues of L (counted according to multiplicity) less than λ.

3-3. Set $d(I + \lambda N, 0, D) = g(\lambda)$. Prove that if $g(\lambda + \varepsilon)$ and $g(\lambda - \varepsilon)$ are both defined and unequal, then $(I - \beta N)x = 0$ has some solution $x \in \partial D$ for $\beta \in (\lambda - \varepsilon, \lambda + \varepsilon)$.

3-4. Let $Tu = \int_G K(x,y)u(y)\, dy$ be a compact mapping of $L_1(G)$ into itself, where $K(x,y) \geq 0$ in G. Prove that T always has a positive eigenvalue and eigenfunction. (Hint: Consider the set of functions $C = \{u(x) \mid u(x) \in L_1(G),\ u(x) \geq 0$ a.e., $\int_G u(x) = 1\}$. Then C is a convex bounded set, and $Tu/\|Tu\|_{L_1}: C \to C$.)

3-5. (Krasnoselski's Fixed Point Theorem) Let H denote a Hilbert space and suppose N is a continuous compact mapping of $H \to H$ which satisfies $(Nx,x) \leq (x,x)$. Prove $Nx = x$ has at least one solution in H. (Hint: Suppose otherwise and consider the homotopy $H(x,t) = tN(x) + I$.)

3-6. (Birkhoff-Kellogg) Let X be a Banach space and $\partial\Sigma_R = \{x \mid \|x\| = R\}$. Suppose N is a compact mapping of $X \to X$ and $\|Nx\| \geq \alpha > 0$ for $x \in \partial\Sigma_R$. Then $x = \lambda Nx$ has a solution x_R with $\|x_R\| = R$. (Hint: Consider the mapping $x \to R(Nx/\|Nx\|)$.)

§3-2. A SPECIAL CLASS OF NONCOMPACT OPERATORS

We now consider the transition to infinite dimensions of the result mentioned in Theorem 2-43 of Section 2-6. The surprising fact here is that this transition can be carried out independently of compactness assumptions on the operators concerned. However, it is interesting to note that an extra condition must be added in the infinite dimensional case.

THEOREM 3-10. _Let_ H _be a real separable Hilbert space, and let_ T _be a bounded continuous mapping from_ H _into itself satisfying the conditions_

(i) $(Tu,u)\|u\|^{-1} \to \infty$ _as_ $\|u\| \to \infty$

(ii) $(Tu - Tv, u - v) \geq 0$ _for all_ $u, v \in H$, _i.e._ T _is monotone_.

Then the equation $Tu = f$ _has a solution for all_ $f \in H$.

Proof. The idea of the proof is to use conditions (i) and Theorem 2-43 of Section 2-6 to find approximations u_m to the solution, and to use condition (ii) to guarantee that these approximations do indeed converge to a solution.

Let $w_1, w_2, \ldots$ be a sequence of orthonormal elements of H so chosen that $\bigcup_m H_m$ is dense in H, where H_m is the linear space generated by $w_1, \ldots, w_m$. For each m, we attempt to find an element $u_m \in H_m$ such that

$$(Tu_m, w) = (f, w) \quad \text{for every} \quad w \in H_m \tag{3-4}$$

To do this, set $P_m u = \Sigma_{j=1}^m (u, w_j) w_j$. Then (3-4) is equivalent to $P_m T u_m = P_m f$. We note that as $\|v\| \to \infty$, $(P_m Tv, v)\|v\| \to \infty$ for $v \in H_m$ follows immediately from (i). Thus by Theorem 2-43 of Section 2-6, there exists $u_m \in H_m$ such that $P_m T u_m = P_m f$, and furthermore $(Tu_m, u_m) = (f, u_m)$. We now consider the passage to the limit. By Schwarz' inequality

$$|(Tu_m, u_m)| = |(f, u_m)| \leq \|f\| \|u_m\|$$

By (i), $\|u_m\| \leq c$, and therefore $\|Tu_m\| \leq c'$. Thus there are subsequences (by virtue of the remarks of Section 3-1), which we again label u_m, such that $u_m \to u$ weakly and $Tu_m \to \chi$ weakly. By (3-4) we deduce that $\chi = f$. Now to show that $Tu = f$. By monotonicity $(u_m - w, Tu_m - Tw) \geq 0$, and by weak convergence $(u_m, Tu_m) = (f, u_m) \to (u, f)$, $(u_m, Tw) \to (u, Tw)$ and $(w, Tu_m) \to (w, f)$ as $m \to \infty$. Thus expanding and letting $m \to \infty$, $(u - w, f - Tw) \geq 0$. Setting $w = u - \lambda z$ for $\lambda > 0$ and z any element of H, we conclude that $\lambda(z, f - T(u - \lambda z)) \geq 0$; that is $(z, f - T(u - \lambda z)) \geq 0$. Letting $\lambda \to 0$, we obtain $(z, f - Tu) \geq 0$. As z is arbitrary, $f = Tu$. ||

Exercises

3-7. Suppose T is a bounded continuous mapping of a real

separable Hilbert space H into itself satisfying

$$(Tu - Tv, u - v) \geq k\|u - v\|^2 \quad \text{for all} \quad u, v \in H$$

where k is a positive constant independent of u and v. Prove that the equation $Tu = f$ is well-posed in the sense that $Tu = f$ has one and only one solution for each $f \in H$ and the solution of this equation depends continuously on f in H.

3-8. Prove an analogue of Theorem 3-10 if $T = T_1 + N$, where N maps weakly convergent sequences into strongly convergent sequences, and if we replace hypothesis (ii) by $(T_1u - T_1v, u - v) \geq 0$.

§3-3. GRADIENT OPERATORS AND THEIR PROPERTIES

The infinite dimensional analogue of a gradient system is a gradient operator. Let T be a continuous mapping of a Hilbert space H into itself. Then T is a gradient operator provided it is the gradient of a real-valued continuous functional $F(u)$ defined on H, that is

$$\lim_{\epsilon \to 0} [F(u + \epsilon v) - F(u)]/\epsilon = (Tu, v)$$

for all $u, v \in H$; and we write $\operatorname{grad} F(u) = Tu$. If $Tu = 0$, the element u is called a critical point of the functional $F(v)$. Just as in the finite dimensional case, local maxima and minima of $F(v)$ are critical points.

An alternative definition is as follows:

THEOREM 3-11. T *is a gradient operator if and only if the following identity holds for all* $u, v \in H$

$$\int_0^1 [(u,T(su)) - (v,T(sv))]ds = \int_0^1 (u-v,T(su + (1-s)v))ds \quad (3\text{-}5)$$

Moreover, $F(u)$ *can be written as* $\int_0^1 (u,T(su))\, ds$.

Proof. If $F(u) = \int_0^1 (u,T(su))\, ds$ and (3-5) holds, then $F(u + \epsilon v) - F(u) = \epsilon\int_0^1 (v,T(u + s\epsilon v))\, ds$. Let $\epsilon \to 0$, then $\lim_{\epsilon\to 0}[F(u + \epsilon v) - F(u)]/\epsilon = (v,Tu)$. Conversely, if T is a gradient operator, then $(d/ds)F(u + sv) = \lim_{\epsilon\to 0}[F(u+(s+\epsilon)v) - F(u+sv)]/\epsilon = (v,T(u + sv))$. Replacing u by v and v by $u - v$ and integrating from 0 to 1 with respect to s, we obtain

$$F(u) - F(v) = \int_0^1 (u - v,T(v + s(u - v))\, ds$$

and setting $v = 0$ and $F(0) = 0$, $F(u) = \int_0^1 (u,T(su))\, ds.$ ||

Note: A linear operator T mapping H into itself is a gradient operator if and only if it is self-adjoint. For if T is linear, formula (3-5) reduces to $(u,Tv) = (v,Tu)$.

Let $\{u_n\}$ denote a sequence of elements of H converging to an element u also in the space H. Then a real-valued functional $\mathfrak{J}(v)$ defined on H is lower semi-continuous with respect to this type of convergence if $\mathfrak{J}(u) \leq \liminf_{n\to\infty} \mathfrak{J}(u_n)$. If whenever $u_n \to u$ weakly in H.

$\mathfrak{J}(u) \leq \liminf_{n\to\infty} \mathfrak{J}(u_n)$, $\mathfrak{J}(u)$ is called lower semi-continuous with respect to weak convergence. The relevance of this concept is clearly seen in the classical theory of the calculus of variations and from the following simple result.

THEOREM 3-12. Let $F(u)$ be a real-valued continuous functional on H such that $F(u)\|u\|^{-1} \to \infty$ as $\|u\| \to \infty$. Then grad $F(u) = p$ has a solution for every $p \in H$, provided F is lower semi-continuous with respect to weak convergence.

Proof. First we note that $F(u) - (p,u) = \mathfrak{J}(u) \to \infty$ as $\|u\| \to \infty$. Also, $c = \inf_H \mathfrak{J}(u)$ is bounded above $-\infty$. Assume there is a sequence $u_n \to u$ weakly such that $\lim_{n\to\infty} \mathfrak{J}(u_n) = c$. Now by the lower semi-continuity of F, $\mathfrak{J}(u) \leq \liminf_{n\to\infty} \mathfrak{J}(u_n)$. Hence there is a subsequence of $\{u_n\}$, $\{u_{n_j}\}$, satisfying

$$\liminf_{n\to\infty} \mathfrak{J}(u_n) = \lim_{n_j\to\infty} \mathfrak{J}(u_{n_j}) = c$$

Therefore, given our assumption, as c is an infimum, $\mathfrak{J}(u) = c$. Thus $\mathfrak{J}$ has a minimum at u, u is a critical point, and grad $\mathfrak{J}(u) =$ grad $F(u) - f = 0$. Now we show that there is a sequence $u_n \to u$ weakly with $\mathfrak{J}(u_n) = c$. First, by definition, there is a sequence u_n such that $\mathfrak{J}(u_n) \to c$; for sufficiently large n, $F(u_n) - (p,u_n) \leq c + 1$ and

$||u_n|| \{F(u_n) ||u_n||^{-1} - ||p||\} \leq c + 1$. This last inequality implie[s] $||u_n||$ is bounded. As H is a Hilbert space, the remarks of Section 3-1 imply u_n has a weakly convergent subsequence (which we relabel u_n) with the property $\mathfrak{F}(u_n) \to c$, as required. ||

LEMMA 3-13. _If_ grad F _is monotone, i.e._ (grad Fu - grad Fv, u - v) ≥ 0, _then_ F _is a convex functional lower semi-continuous with respect to weak convergence_.

Proof. Denote grad F(u) by f(u). By Theorem 3-11,

$$F(u_n) - F(u) = \int_0^1 (u_n - u, f(u + s(u_n - u)))ds$$

$$= \int_0^1 (u_n - u, f(u))ds + \int_0^1 (u_n - u, f(u + s(u_n - u)) - f(u))ds$$

Hence if u_n converges weakly to u, as $n \to \infty$ the first term on the right side of the latter expression tends to 0. The second term is always nonnegative. Indeed by monotonicit[y] $(s(u_n - u), f(u + s(u_n - u)) - f(u)) \geq 0$ $(0 \leq s \leq 1)$, and thus the integrand is always nonegative for $0 \leq s \leq 1$. Hence for sufficiently large n, $F(u_n) - F(u) \geq -\epsilon_n^2$ where $\epsilon_n \to 0$ as $n \to \infty$ so that $\liminf_{n\to\infty} F(u_n) \geq F(u)$.

To prove convexity, we use Theorem 3-11 for $0 \leq t \leq 1$ to write

$$F(tu+(1-t)v) - F(v) = \int_0^1 (t(u-v), f(v+st(u-v))ds$$

$$\leq t\int_0^1 (u-v, f(v+s(u-v)))ds \quad \text{(by monotonicity)}$$

$$\leq t(F(u) - F(v)) \qquad \text{(by Theorem 3-11)}$$

Thus rearranging terms we have

$$F(tu + (1-t)v) \leq tF(u) + (1-t)F(v) \qquad \text{for } 0 \leq t \leq 1 \;\|$$

We next consider gradient operators with constraints. First some definitions and a lemma.

An operator A is <u>completely continuous</u> if A maps weakly convergent sequences into strongly convergent sequences. In a Hilbert space we note that complete continuity implies compactness and continuity. The converse is not true (see Exercise 3-9 below).

A functional $F(u)$ is <u>continuous with respect to weak convergence</u> if $u_n \to u$ weakly implies $F(u_n) \to F(u)$. This insures that on any bounded set, F is bounded.

(Note: A functional continuous with respect to weak convergence is continuous with respect to convergence in norm, but the converse is not generally true.)

LEMMA 3-14. <u>If the gradient of a functional</u> $F(u)$ <u>is completely continuous</u>, $F(u)$ <u>is continuous with respect to weak</u>

convergence.

Proof. Let $u_n \to u$ weakly and denote grad $F(u)$ by $f(u)$, then as in the proof of Lemma 3-13,

$$F(u_n) - F(u) = \int_0^1 (u_n-u, f(u))ds + \int_0^1 (u_n-u, f(u+s(u_n-u))-f(u))d$$

The first term tends to 0 as n tends to ∞, by weak convergence. The second term also tends to 0. Indeed, by the complete continuity of f, $\|f(u+s(u_n-u)) - f(u)\| \to 0$; and by property (b) of weak convergence (Definitions 3-1), $\|u_n - u\|$ is uniformly bounded. ||

The following result proves an infinite dimensional analogue of Theorem 2-27 on invariant directions on manifolds. We will consider manifolds $\mathfrak{M}$ (in the Hilbert space H) of the form $\mathfrak{M} = \{u | u \in H, F(u) = R\}$, where R is a fixed real number and $F(u)$ is a real-valued functional defined on H with grad $F \neq 0$ on $\mathfrak{M}$. For example if $F(u) = (u,u)$, then $\mathfrak{M} = \partial\Sigma_R$ the sphere of radius $\sqrt{R}$ in H. A critical point u_0 of a functional $G(u)$ on the manifold $\mathfrak{M}$ is a solution on $\mathfrak{M}$ of the equation grad$[G(u) + \lambda F(u)] = 0$ (cf. 2-26). Alternately, if $\lambda \neq 0$, we can write grad$[F(u) + \lambda G(u)] = 0$. Note, as a special case, that a critical point of $G(u)$ on the sphere $\partial\Sigma_R$ is an invariant direction of grad $G(u)$ on $\partial\Sigma_R$, that is a solution u on $\partial\Sigma_R$ of grad $G(u) = -\lambda u$.

THEOREM 3-15. *Suppose* (i) $F(u) \to \infty$ *as* $\|u\| \to \infty$, grad $F(u)$ *is monotone and continuous in* H, *and* $(\text{grad } F(u),u) \neq 0$ *for* $u \neq 0$. *Suppose also that* (ii) grad $G(u)$ *is a completely continuous operator such that* grad $F(0) = 0$, *and* (iii) $(\text{grad } G(u),u) > 0$ *for* $u \neq 0$. *Then for every* $c > 0$ *there exists a* $u_c \in H$ *with* $F(u_c) = c$ *and*

$$\text{grad } F(u_c) = \lambda \text{grad } G(u_c) \tag{3-6}$$

where λ *is a real number*; *that is*, *there is a one parameter family of solutions* u_c *of* (3-6) *each solution being a critical point of* $G(u)$ *on the manifold* $\partial\Sigma_c = \{u|F(u) = c\}$.

Proof. The proof is divided into two parts. In Part 1 we solve the variational problem $\sup G(u)$ over $\partial\Sigma_c$ for fixed $c > 0$. Call u_c the solution. In Part 2 we show u_c is a critical point of the functional $G(u)$ on the manifold $\partial\Sigma_c$.

Part 1. We may assume that $F(0) = G(0) = 0$. Let c be a positive real number and $\Sigma_c = \{u|u \in H, F(u) \leq c\}$. Σ_c is closed bounded and convex and $\partial\Sigma_c = \{u|u \in H, F(u) = c\}$. Note that $\partial\Sigma_c$ is non-vacuous as $F(u)$ is continuous, $F(0) = 0$, and $F(tu) \to \infty$ as $t \to \infty$. By Lemma 3-14, $G(u)$ is continuous w.r.t. weak convergence and thus maps the bounded set $\partial\Sigma_c$ into a bounded set of real numbers. Hence $\sup_{\partial\Sigma_c} G(u) = \alpha < \infty$, and there is a sequence $u_n \in \partial\Sigma_c$ such that $G(u_n) \to \alpha$. As $\partial\Sigma_c$ is bounded, a subsequence $\{u_{n_j}\}$ is weakly convergent in H to some element u_c. Therefore $G(u_c) = \alpha$, and $\alpha > 0$ follows from (iii) and the representation $G(u) = \int_0^1 (u, \text{grad } G(su))\, ds$. By Lemma 3-13, $F(u)$ is lower semi-continuous w.r.t. weak convergence and $F(u_c) \leq \liminf_{n\to\infty} F(u_n) = c$, that is $u_c \in \Sigma_c$. Since $\alpha > 0$, $u_c \neq 0$. We show that $u_c \in \partial\Sigma_c$. If not, then $tu_c \in \partial\Sigma_c$ for $t > 1$ as Σ_c is convex; and

$$G(tu_c) - G(u_c) = (t-1)\int_0^1 (u_c, \text{ grad } G(ku_c))\, ds \;>\; 0$$

where $k = 1 + s(t - 1) \geq 1$. Hence $G(tu_c) > G(u_c) = \sup_{\partial\Sigma_c} G(u)$, a contradiction.

<u>Part 2</u>. We now prove that u_c is a critical point of $G(x)$ on $\partial\Sigma_c$, that is, that (3-6) holds. To accomplish this, we show that if (3-6) does not hold, then $G(u)$ can be increased beyond $G(u_c)$ for $u \in \partial\Sigma_c$. Let us therefore consider small arcs on $\partial\Sigma_c$, centered at u_c, of the form $h(t) = u_c + tv + a(t)u_c$; where v is an arbitrary element o H, and $a(t)$ is chosen so that $a(0) = 0$ and $h(t) \in \partial\Sigma_c$ for small $|t|$. Such a function $a(t)$ exists because the condition $F(h(t)) = c$ implies

$$(d/dt)F(h(t)) = (\text{grad } F(h(t)), v + a'(t)u_c) = 0$$

that is, $a(t)$ is a solution of the nonlinear ordinary differential equation

$$a'(t) = \frac{(\text{grad } F(h(t)),v)}{(\text{grad } F(h(t)),u_c)} \tag{3-7}$$

with $a(0) = 0$. As $(\text{grad } F(u_c),u_c) \neq 0$, for small $|t|$, $(\text{grad } F(h(t)),u_c) \neq 0$. Hence the right side of (3-7) is a continuous function for small $|t|$; and therefore (3-7) does indeed have a solution for small $|t|$. Now we choose v so that $(v,\text{grad } F(u_c)) = 0$. Then $a'(0) = 0$ and $a'(t) \to 0$ as $|t| \to 0$. Next, we compare the values $G(h(t))$ and $G(u_c)$. By the Mean Value Theorem, $a(t) = a'(\theta)t$ where $0 < |\theta| < |t|$; and denoting $(v + a'(\theta)u_c)$ by z,

$$\begin{aligned} G(u_c+tv+a(t)u_c) - G(u_c) &= t\int_0^1 (v+a'(\theta)u_c,\text{grad } G(u_c+stz))\, ds \\ &= t\int_0^1 [(v,\text{grad } G(u_c)) + O(t)]\, ds \end{aligned}$$

Now let $|t| \to 0$ and suppose $(v,\text{grad } G(u_c)) = \beta \neq 0$, then each of the last two terms tends to 0. Therefore for $|t|$ sufficiently small,

$$G(u_c + tv + a(t)u_c) - G(u_c) = t(\beta + O(t))$$

Thus the sign of the right hand side of the last equality depends on the sign of t, contrary to the maximality of

$G(u_c)$ on $\partial\Sigma_c$. Hence

$$(v, \text{grad } F(u_c)) = 0 \quad \text{implies} \quad (v, \text{grad } G(u_c)) = 0 \tag{3-8}$$

As H is a Hilbert space, we can write $\text{grad } G(u_c) = \lambda \text{grad } F(u_c) + \bar{v}$ where $(\bar{v}, \text{grad } F(u_c)) = 0$. So $(\bar{v}, \text{grad } G(u_c)) = \|\bar{v}\|^2 = 0$ (by (3-8)). Thus $\bar{v} = 0$ and $\text{grad } G(u_c) = \lambda \text{grad } F(u_c)$ where λ is a real number. $\|$

Exercises

3-9. In $L_2[0,1]$ there is a continuous compact mapping N which is not completely continuous. (Hint: Define $Nu(s) = \int_0^1 K(s,t)u^2(t)\, dt$, where $K(s,t)$ is continuous in $[0,1] \times [0,1]$ and $0 < m \leq K(s,t) \leq M$.)

3-10. Let L be a compact self-adjoint operator mapping a Hilbert space H into itself with $(Lu,u) > 0$ for $\|u\| \neq 0$. Show that L is a gradient operator, and use Theorem 3-15 to construct the smallest characteristic value λ_1 of $u = \lambda Lu$.

3-11. Suppose N is a completely continuous gradient operato mapping H into itself with $\|Nu\| \leq k\|u\|^{1+\sigma}$ for $\sigma > 0$ and $\|u\|$ sufficiently small. If $(Nu,u) > 0$ for $u \neq 0$, prove that the equation $u = \lambda(Lu + Nu)$ has a one parameter family of solutions $u(c)$ with $\|u\| = c$ such that $\lambda(c) \to \lambda_1$, as $c \to 0$ (where λ_1 is as in Exercise 3-10 above.)

3-12. (Banach) Let $(A(x_1,\ldots,x_n),x_{n+1})$ be a multilinear mapping of $\Pi_{i=1}^{n+1} H_i \to \mathbb{R}^1$ which is symmetric under all permutations of its arguments, where ΠH_i denotes the direct sum of $n + 1$ copies of H. Suppose $A(x,x,\ldots,x) = Ax$ is a completely continuous mapping of $H \to H$ with $(Ax,x) > 0$ for $x \neq 0$. Prove $x = \lambda Ax$ has a solution $(x_c, \lambda(c))$ with $\|x_c\| = c$ for every $c > 0$. (Hint: Show Ax is a gradient operator and apply Theorem 3-15.)

3-13. Prove an analogue of Theorem 3-15 by finding a critical point of $F(u)$ on the hypersurface $\partial B_c = \{u | G(u) = c\}$ for any $c > 0$.

§3-4. A REMARK ON THE THEORY OF CRITICAL POINTS OF INFINITE DIMENSIONAL GRADIENT OPERATORS

Analogues of the results of Theorems 2-32 and 2-33 hold for infinite dimensional gradient operators defined on manifolds provided certain restrictive hypotheses are added. An example of such a hypothesis occurs in Theorem 3-12, where in order to extend the result of Exercise 2-13 to infinite dimensions, the concept of lower semi-continuity with respect to weak convergence was required. Clearly the results mentioned above depend heavily on the geometry of infinite dimensional manifolds $\mathfrak{M}$. It is exactly at this point that rather unusual infinite dimensional phenomena occur. Consider for example the unit sphere $\Sigma = \{x | \|x\| \leq 1\}$. Then Example 3-2 implies that there is a continuous mapping of Σ onto $\partial\Sigma = \{x | \|x\| = 1\}$ leaving all points on $\partial\Sigma$ fixed: An impossible fact in finite dimensions.

Many infinite dimensional results on critical points and their estimation have been carried out using the axiom schemes of Morse or Ljusternik-Schnirelmann in Section 2-3. An important restriction in such results is the so-called (Condition C) of Palais and Smale. In the context of Theorem 3-15 Condition C is a hypothesis on the closure of $\mathfrak{M} = \{u | F(u) = R\}$ with respect to weak convergence; namely if a weakly convergent sequence on $\mathfrak{M}$ has limit u and $\operatorname{grad} F(u_n) \to \operatorname{grad} F(u)$ strongly, then $u_n \to u$ strongly, so that $u \in \mathfrak{M}$. For example if $F(u) = \|u\|^2 + M(u)$ where $\operatorname{grad} M(u)$ is a completely continuous operator, Condition C is automatically satisfied. For more details see the research papers mentioned in the bibliography.

§3-5. LOCAL BEHAVIOR OF NONLINEAR OPERATOR EQUATIONS IN HILBERT SPACE

Here we investigate another situation in which infinite dimensional problems can be reduced to nonlinear systems of finite dimension. Although this finite dimensional system may be complicated, the methods of Chapter 2 often yield important facts not readily obtainable by other means.

We wish to investigate the totality of real solutions of the nonlinear operator equation $F(u,\lambda) = 0$ in the neighborhood of a given solution $u_0(\lambda)$ as a function of a real parameter λ. Here $F(u,\lambda)$ is a continuous mapping of a real Hilbert space H into itself, for fixed λ. Furthermore, for simplicity, we assume $F(u,\lambda)$ depends linearly on λ so $F(u,\lambda) = \mathfrak{N}_1 u - \lambda \mathfrak{N}_2 u$. If $\mathfrak{N}_1$ is the identity mapping and $\mathfrak{N}_2$ is linear $(u_0(\lambda) \equiv 0)$ then our investigation coincides with the "spectral" theory of the operator $\mathfrak{N}_2$, (for example the determination of the eigenvalues and eigenvectors of $\mathfrak{N}_2$). Furthermore in the linear case "local" results (that is for solutions with $\|u(\lambda) - u_0(\lambda)\|$ small) coincide with the so-called "global" results (i.e. solutions with $\|u(\lambda) - u_0(\lambda)\|$ large).

The extension of these ideas to a nonlinear context is a difficult mathematical problem. However certain aspects can be studied by our techniques. We begin with the following definition.

DEFINITION 3-16. <u>Suppose that the equation</u> $F(u,\lambda) = 0$ <u>possesses at least two distinct solutions</u> $u_0(\lambda)$ <u>and</u> $u_1(\lambda)$ <u>such that</u> $u_1(\lambda) \to u_0(\lambda)$ <u>as</u> $\lambda \to \lambda_0$, <u>then the real number</u> λ_0 <u>is called a bifurcation point of the equation</u> $F(u,\lambda) = 0$ <u>with respect to</u> $u_0(\lambda)$. <u>The families of solutions</u> $u_1(\lambda)$ <u>and</u> $u_0(\lambda)$ <u>are called branches of solutions bifurcating from</u> λ_0.

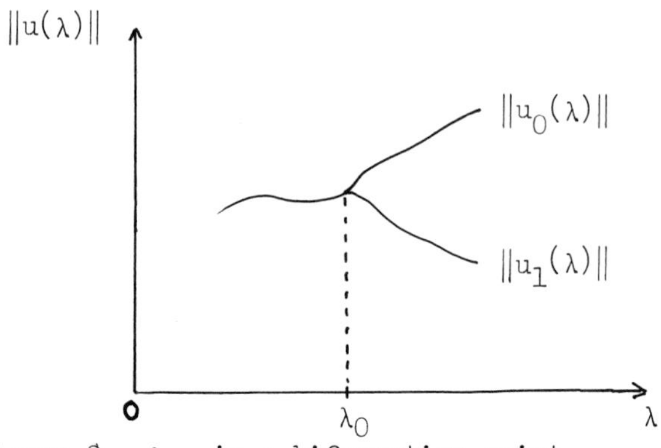

Figure 8. λ_0 is a bifurcation point.

We wish to investigate the relationship between the loca behavior of solutions of $F(u,\lambda) = \mathfrak{N}_1 u + \lambda \mathfrak{N}_2 u = 0$ near $u_0(\lambda$ and its "linearization"[4] about $u_0(\lambda)$. Without loss of generality we may assume $u_0(\lambda) \equiv 0$ so that $F(0,\lambda) \equiv 0$ for al λ. (Otherwise we consider $v = u - u_0(\lambda)$). To this end, we introduce the following restrictions on $\mathfrak{N}_1$ and $\mathfrak{N}_2$.

(i) $\mathfrak{N}_1$ is the identity operator on H (after possibly introducing an equivalent inner product in H).

(ii) $\mathfrak{N}_2$ is a completely continuous mapping.

(iii) $\mathfrak{N}_2$ has a nondegenerate linearization, more precisely, $\mathfrak{N}_2 u = Lu + Nu$ where L is a bounded linear mapping of H into H and $Lu \neq 0$ for $u \neq 0$, N is a bounded

---

[4] By the linearization of an operator $F(u)$ at a point $u_0 \in$ we mean the operator $L_{u_0}(u) = \lim_{\epsilon\to 0}[F(u_0+\epsilon u) - F(u_0)]/\epsilon$; (i this limit exists and is linear in u for all $u \in H$.)

mapping of H into H and $\|Nu - Nv\| \leq f(\|u\|, \|v\|)\|u - v\|$ for all u, v with $\|u\|, \|v\|$ sufficiently small and $f(s,t) = O(|s| + |t|)$ is a real-valued continuous function of the real variables s and t.

With these preliminaries completed, we now state

LEMMA 3-17. *The bifurcation points of* $u = \lambda(Lu + Nu)$ *with respect to* $u_0(\lambda) \equiv 0$ *can occur only at eigenvalues of the linearized equation* $u = \lambda Lu$.

Proof. Suppose λ_0 is not an eigenvalue of the linear equation $u = \lambda Lu$, then we shall show that for $|\lambda - \lambda_0|$ and $\|u\|$ sufficiently small, $u = \lambda(Lu + Nu)$ has the unique solution $u \equiv 0$. Indeed, as L is a bounded operator $\|Lu\| \leq \|L\|\|u\|$; and as $I - \lambda_0 L$ is invertible, there is an integer $k > 0$ and independent of $u \in H$ such that $\|(I - \lambda_0 L)u\| \geq k\|u\|$, (see Appendix II). Thus

$$\|u - \lambda_0 Lu\| = \|u - \lambda(Lu + Nu) + (\lambda - \lambda_0)Lu + \lambda Nu\|$$

so that

$$\begin{aligned}\|u - \lambda(Lu + Nu)\| &\geq \|(I - \lambda_0 L)u\| - |\lambda - \lambda_0|\|Lu\| - |\lambda|\|Nu\| \\ &\geq k\|u\| - |\lambda - \lambda_0|\|L\|\|u\| - O(\|u\|^2) \\ &\geq (k - |\lambda - \lambda_0|\|L\| - O(\|u\|))\|u\|\end{aligned}$$

Hence the result follows provided $|\lambda - \lambda_0|$ and $\|u\|$ are sufficiently small, so that $k > |\lambda - \lambda_0| \|L\| + O(\|u\|)$. ||

We now wish to focus attention on the behavior of solutions of $u = \lambda(Lu + Nu)$ for λ near the eigenvalues of $u = \lambda Lu$. To this end we shall need the following lemma.

LEMMA 3-18. _Let_ λ_n _be an eigenvalue of the compact operator_ L, _then_ $E_n = \{u | Lu = \lambda_n^{-1} u\}$ _has finite dimension_.

Proof. Suppose the contrary, namely the existence of a sequence $\{u_m\}$ such that

$$Lu_m = \lambda_n^{-1} u_m \quad \text{and} \quad (u_m, u_k) = \delta_{mk}$$

Then by the compactness of L, $\{Lu_m\}$ has a convergent subsequence which we again label Lu_m; but

$$\lim_{m,q\to\infty} \|Lu_m - Lu_{m+q}\| = \lim_{m,q\to\infty} \lambda_n^{-1} \|u_m - u_{m+q}\| = 2\lambda_n^{-1} \neq 0$$

a contradiction. ||

We shall be concerned with five questions regarding the equation $u = \lambda(Lu + Nu)$.

(1) _Existence Theory_. The determination of _which_ eigenvalues λ_n of $u = \lambda Lu$ are bifurcation points of $u = \lambda(Lu + Nu)$ with respect to $u_0(\lambda)$.

(2) _Multiplicity Theory_. The determination of the

number of branches of solutions $u(\lambda)$ bifurcating from a given point of bifurcation with respect to $u_0(\lambda)$.

(3) Spectral Theory. The description of the behavior of the branches $u(\lambda)$ bifurcating from λ_n as a function of $(\lambda - \lambda_n)$.

(4) Problem of Nonlinear Invariants. What qualitative features of the operator N play a significant role in answering the above questions (1), (2), (3)?

(5) Problems of Linearization. What information concerning questions (1), (2), (3) can be determined from a complete knowledge of the solutions of the linearized problem $u = \lambda Lu$?

The following result shows the extent to which the infinite dimensional problems considered here can be reduced to the solution of a finite dimensional problem.

THEOREM 3-19. *The solutions of small norm of* $u = \lambda(Lu + Nu)$ *in the neighborhood of* λ_n *are determined by the solutions of a finite number* (r) *of nonlinear equations in* (r) *unknowns, where* r *is the multiplicity of the eigenvalue* λ_n.

Proof. For simplicity, we assume L is self-adjoint; that is $(Lu,v) = (u,Lv)$ for all $u, v \in H$. In case L is not self-adjoint an analogous but less explicit proof can be given. Choose r linearly independent eigenfunctions of $u = \lambda_n Lu$ and suppose $(u_i, u_j) = \delta_{ij}$ $(i,j = 1,\ldots,r)$. Let the subspace spanned by $(u_1,\ldots,u_r)$ be denoted $[u_1,\ldots,u_r]$ and its orthogonal complement in H be denoted $[u_1,\ldots,u_r]^{\perp}$. Furthermore let $P\colon H \to [u_1,\ldots,u_r]^{\perp}$ denote the projector of H onto $[u_1,\ldots,u_r]^{\perp}$. Set $\mu = 1/\lambda$. Thus the totality of solutions of the equations $\mu u - Lu - Nu = 0$ can be obtained by solving the $(r + 1)$ equations

$$\begin{aligned} P(\mu u - Lu - Nu) &= 0 \\ (\mu u - Lu - Nu, u_i) &= 0 \qquad (i = 1,\ldots,r) \end{aligned} \tag{3-9}$$

Furthermore any real solution u of this system can be written

$$u = y + \sum_{i=1}^{r} \epsilon_i u_i$$

where $y \in [u_1,\ldots,u_r]^{\perp}$ and ϵ_i are real numbers to be determined. Substituting this expression into (3-9) we obtain the following equations for y and ϵ_i

$$y = (\mu I - L)^{-1} P(N(y + \Sigma \epsilon_i u_i)) \tag{3-10}$$

$$\epsilon_i(\mu - \mu_n) = (N(y + \Sigma \epsilon_i u_i), u_i) \tag{3-11}$$

To proceed further we must assume that we are only concerned with solutions of small norm, that is, that $||y||$ and all the numbers ϵ_i are small compared to 1. The basic idea is to reduce the system (3-10) - (3-11) to the finite dimensional study of r equations (not necessarily linear) in r unknowns by showing that the equation (3-10) is uniquely solvable if the ϵ_i are sufficiently small. This is accomplished by

LEMMA 3-20. <u>Under the above hypotheses, and for fixed</u> μ, <u>the equation</u> (3-10) <u>is uniquely solvable for</u> y <u>in terms of</u> $(\epsilon_1, \ldots, \epsilon_r)$. <u>Furthermore the following estimate holds for the solution</u> $y = y(\epsilon_1, \ldots, \epsilon_r)$

$$\|y\| = O(|\epsilon|^2) \tag{3-12}$$

<u>where</u> $|\epsilon| = |\epsilon_1| + \ldots + |\epsilon_r|$.

<u>Proof</u>. The solutions of equation (3-10) are precisely the fixed points of the mapping

$$T_\epsilon y = (\mu I - L)^{-1} P(N(y + \Sigma \epsilon_i u_i))$$

By the contraction mapping principle (see Appendix II) this equation has one and only one fixed point provided that for $|\epsilon|$ sufficiently small (i) $\|T_\epsilon y - T_\epsilon \bar{y}\| \leq k(\epsilon)\|y - \bar{y}\|$ where $k(\epsilon) < 1$ is a positive constant independent of y and $\bar{y}$ and (ii) T_ϵ maps the sphere $\Sigma_\epsilon = \{y \mid \|y\| \leq |\epsilon|\}$ into itself. Hence we estimate as follows. Let y and $\bar{y}$ belong to Σ_ϵ, then

$$\|T_\epsilon y - T_\epsilon \bar{y}\| \leq \|(\mu I - L)^{-1}P\| \|N(y+\Sigma\epsilon_i u_i) - N(\bar{y}+\Sigma\epsilon_i u_i)\|$$

$$\leq Kf(\|y+\Sigma\epsilon_i u_i\|, \|\bar{y}+\Sigma\epsilon_i u_i\|)\|y-\bar{y}\|$$

$$= O(|\epsilon|)\|y-\bar{y}\|$$

Thus (i) follows by choosing $|\epsilon|$ sufficiently small. It remains to show that $\|T_\epsilon y\| \leq |\epsilon|$ for $\|y\| \leq |\epsilon|$. Indeed,

$$\|T_\epsilon y\| \leq Kf(\|y + \Sigma\epsilon_i u_i\|, 0)\|y + \Sigma\epsilon_i u_i\|$$

So $\|T_\epsilon y\| = O(|\epsilon|^2)$, and $\|T_\epsilon y\| \leq |\epsilon|$ for $|\epsilon|$ sufficiently small. Hence T_ϵ is a contraction mapping defined on the sphere $\|y\| \leq |\epsilon|$. Furthermore we prove the following estimate for the solution of $T_\epsilon y = y$ with $\|y\| \leq |\epsilon|$:

$$\|y\| = \|T_\epsilon y - T_0 y + T_0 y\|$$

$$\leq \|T_\epsilon y - T_0 y\| + \|T_0 y\|$$

$$\leq K[\|N(u) - N(y)\| + \|N(y)\|]$$

$$\leq K[f(\|u\|, \|y\|)\|u - y\| + f(\|y\|, 0)\|y\|]$$

Hence $\|y\| = O(|\epsilon|^2)$ and this completes the proof. ||

The final step in the proof of Theorem 3-19, is the observation that for given μ the system (3-10) - (3-11) can be written in the form

$$\epsilon_i(\mu - \mu_n) = f_i(\epsilon_1, \ldots, \epsilon_r) \quad (i = 1, \ldots, r)$$

where the continuous functions f_i are completely determined by $(\epsilon_1,\ldots,\epsilon_r)$, μ, and the solution y is determined by the lemma. ||

Remark. If hypothesis (iii) is strengthened by assuming $\|Nu - Nv\| \leq K\{\|u\|^p + \|v\|^p\}\|u - v\|$ for constants K and $p > 1$ and independent of u and v, then the estimate of Lemma 3-20 is $\|y\| = O(|\epsilon|^{p+1})$.

The above method is interesting because for many qualitative problems an explicit knowledge of y is unnecessary. For example, we have the following corollary.

COROLLARY 3-21. _Suppose_ (i) $(N(u),u) > 0$ _for_ $u \neq 0$, (ii) N _is a completely continuous mapping homogeneous of degree_ $p + 1$ _that is_ $N(\sigma u) = \sigma^{p+1}Nu$ _for fixed positive_ p, _and_ (iii) _the hypothesis of the above remark is satisfied_. _Then any nonzero solution of small norm of_ $u = \lambda(Lu + Nu)$ _with_ λ _in the neighborhood of_ λ_n _occurs with_ $\lambda < \lambda_n$.

Proof. Since $u \neq 0$, $|\epsilon| \neq 0$; for if $|\epsilon| = 0$, the estimate (3-12) implies $y = 0$ and as all small solutions are of the form $u = y + \Sigma\epsilon_i u_i$, $u \equiv 0$. By Theorem 3-19, it is sufficient to consider the r equations (3-11)

$$\epsilon_i(\mu - \mu_n) = (N(y + \Sigma\epsilon_i u_i),u_i)$$

Furthermore these equations can be written

$$\epsilon_i(\mu-\mu_n) = (N(\Sigma\epsilon_i u_i),u_i) - (R,u_i) \quad (i = 1,\dots,r) \tag{3-13}$$

where $R = N(y + \Sigma\epsilon_i u_i) - N(\Sigma\epsilon_i u_i)$. By the Cauchy Schwarz inequality, hypothesis (iii), and estimate (3-12)

$$|(R,u_i)| \leq \|R\| = O(|\epsilon|^{2p+1}) \tag{3-14}$$

Now multiplying each equation of system (3-13) by ϵ_i and summing

$$(\Sigma\epsilon_i^2)(\mu-\mu_n) = (N(\Sigma\epsilon_i u_i),\Sigma\epsilon_i u_i) + (R,\Sigma\epsilon_i u_i) \tag{3-15}$$

From (3-14) we find that

$$|(R,\Sigma\epsilon_i u_i)| = O(|\epsilon|^{2p+2}) \tag{3-16}$$

and to show that $\mu > \mu_n$ we estimate the first term on the right of equation (3-15) as follows. Define $\epsilon_i = |\epsilon|\bar{\epsilon}_i$ for then $|\bar{\epsilon}| = 1$ and by hypothesis (ii) $N(\Sigma\epsilon_i u_i) = N(|\epsilon|\Sigma\bar{\epsilon}_i u_i) = |\epsilon|^{p+1}N(\Sigma\bar{\epsilon}_i u_i)$. On the other hand, by hypothesis (i)

$$\begin{aligned}(N(\Sigma\epsilon_i u_i),\Sigma\epsilon_i u_i) &= |\epsilon|^{p+2}(N(\Sigma\bar{\epsilon}_i u_i),\Sigma\bar{\epsilon}_i u_i) \\ &\geq |\epsilon|^{p+2} \inf_{|\bar{\epsilon}_i|=1} (N(\Sigma\bar{\epsilon}_i u_i),\Sigma\bar{\epsilon}_i u_i) \\ &\geq C|\epsilon|^{p+2}\end{aligned} \tag{3-17}$$

where $C > 0$. Therefore from (3-15) and (3-16)

$$(\Sigma \epsilon_i^2)(\mu - \mu_n) \geq C|\epsilon|^{p+2} - k_0''|\epsilon|^{2p+1} = |\epsilon|^{p+2}[C - k_0''|\epsilon|^{p-1}]$$

Thus for sufficiently small $\epsilon \neq 0$, $(\mu-\mu_n)$ is positive and so for a nonzero solution of the system (3-11) $\mu > \mu_n$, that is $\lambda < \lambda_n$. ||

We shall end this section with a brief survey of other methods that can be used to answer questions regarding solutions of the equation $u = \lambda(Lu + Nu)$. For simplicity we restrict attention to the problem of existence mentioned above, that is the determination of those eigenvalues λ_n which are bifurcation points of the equation $u = \lambda(Lu + Nu)$ with respect to $u_0(\lambda) \equiv 0$.

THEOREM 3-22. _If_ λ_n _is simple, that is the eigenspace of_ $u = \lambda_n Lu$ _is one-dimensional, then_ λ_n _is a point of bifurcation of_ $u = \lambda(Lu + Nu)$ _with respect to_ $u \equiv 0$.

Proof. This result is obtained by means of the degree of a mapping. Indeed, we obtain a contradiction by assuming the only solution of $u = \lambda(Lu + Nu)$ near λ_n with $\|u\|$ sufficiently small is $u = 0$. For then if $\Sigma_\epsilon = \{u \mid \|u\| \leq \epsilon\}$ is any sphere with ϵ sufficiently small and λ near λ_n, $g(\lambda) = d(I - \lambda(L + N), 0, \Sigma_\epsilon)$ is constant with respect to λ

(see Exercise 3-3). On the other hand, as $\delta \neq 0$ is small

$$d(I - (\lambda_n + \delta)(L + N), 0, \Sigma_\epsilon) = d(I - (\lambda_n + \delta)L, 0, \Sigma_\epsilon)$$

This equation follows by considering the homotopy $H(x,t)$ and the property of homotopy invariance of degree, where

$$H(x,t) = [I - (\lambda_n + \delta)L - t(\lambda_n + \delta)N]u$$

However, by Exercise 3-2, for $\delta > 0$ and sufficiently small

$$d(I - (\lambda_n - \delta)L, 0, \Sigma_\epsilon) = (-1)^\beta$$

$$d(I - (\lambda_n + \delta)L, 0, \Sigma_\epsilon) = (-1)^{\beta+1}$$

The above two equations contradict the fact that $g(\lambda)$ is constant.

THEOREM 3-23. *If* λ_n *is the smallest eigenvalue of* $u = \lambda Lu$ *with* L *self-adjoint, then* λ_n *is a point of bifurcation of* $u = \lambda(Lu + Nu)$ *with respect to* $u_0(\lambda) \equiv 0$, *provided* N *is a gradient operator.*

Proof. The proof of this result is contained in Exercises 3-10 and 3-11 of Section 3-3.

More generally we note the following result without proof.

THEOREM 3-24. (Krasnoselski) *Let* L *be a self-adjoint operator and* N *be a gradient operator. Then all eigenvalues of* L *are points of bifurcation of* $u = \lambda(Lu + Nu)$ *with respect to* $u_0(\lambda) \equiv 0$.

(For the proof the reader is referred to [6, p. 332].

Exercises

3-14. Consider the following system of equations in $\mathbb{R}^n$

$$u = \lambda Lu + N_1(u,v)$$

$$v = \lambda Lv + N_2(u,v)$$

where L is a self-adjoint positive definite matrix, u and v are vectors in $\mathbb{R}^n$ and N_1 and N_2 are real analytic functions of u and v whose power series expansions about the origin begin with quadratic terms.

(a) If $(v,N_1) + (u,N_2) \neq 0$ $(u, v \neq 0)$, show that the system has no solution other than $(0,0)$.

(b) Find conditions on N_1 and N_2 that guarantee the existence of nonzero solutions u, v with $|u| + |v|$ sufficiently small and λ near λ_1 (λ_1 is the smallest eigenvalue of the matrix L).

(c) Generalize these results to a Hilbert space H over the real numbers.

3-15. Generalize the results of this section to equations of the form $u + Nu = \lambda Lu$ where N and L satisfy the hypothsses (i), (ii), (iii) of pages 120-121.

3-16. Under the hypotheses of Corollary 3-21, investigate the existence and multiplicity of solutions of $u = \lambda(Lu + Nu)$ near a simple eigenvalue of $u = \lambda Lu$.

3-16. (On Fredholm Operators) A Fredholm operator is a bounded linear mapping A of a Banach space B into itself with the following properties

(i) the dimension of $\ker A = \{x \mid x \in B, Ax = 0\}$ is finite

(ii) the range of A is closed

(iii) the dimension of coker $A < \infty$ where coker A is the subspace $B/\text{Range } A$.

If $A = I + L$ where L is a compact linear mapping of B into itself, prove A is Fredholm. The index of a Fredholm operator A (denoted $\text{ind}(A)$) is defined to be the integer $\text{ind}(A) = \dim \ker A - \dim \text{coker } A$. Prove

(a) that $\text{ind}(A)$ is stable under compact perturbations i.e. $\text{ind}(A) = \text{ind}(A + L)$ if L is linear and compact (see Kato, Perturbation Theory for Linear Operators, p. 238).

(b) if B is finite dimensional, $\text{ind}(A) = 0$;

(c) if $\|A - \tilde{A}\|$ is sufficiently small, then $\text{ind}(A) = \text{ind}(\tilde{A})$.

For an interesting nonlinear analogue of Fredholm operators see [7].

Bibliography

1. F. Riesz and B. Sz.-Nagy, Functional Analysis, Ungar, New York, 1955.
2. R. S. Palais, Morse theory on Banach manifolds, Topology 2 (1963) 299-340.
3. R.S. Palais, Ljusternik-Schnirelmann theory on Banach manifolds, Topology 5 (1966) 115-132.
4. J. T. Schwartz, Generalizing the Ljusternik-Schnirelmann theory of critical points, Comm. Pure & Appl. Math. 17 (1964) 307 - 315.
5. S. Smale, Morse Theory and a nonlinear generalization of the Dirichlet problem, Annals of Math. 80 (1962) 332-396.
6. M. A. Krasnoselski, Topological Methods in the Theory of nonlinear integral equations, Pergamon, New York, 1964.
7. S. Smale, An infinite dimensional generalization of Sard's Theorem, American J. Math. 87 (1965) 861-866.

CHAPTER 4

APPLICATIONS

Nonlinear problems arise naturally throughout many areas of knowledge. The ideas presented in the first three chapters of this book give valuable qualitative insights and unity to otherwise seemingly disjoint and intractable scientific situations. The purpose of this chapter is to give a brief introduction to the applications of these ideas in specific instances.

§4-1. GLOBAL UNIVALENCE

Let $f(x)$ be a continuously differentiable mapping of $\mathbb{R}^n$ into itself. Suppose the Jacobian determinant of $f(x)$, $\det |J_f(x)| > 0$ for any x in a bounded open set D in $\mathbb{R}^n$. Then, by the Implicit Function Theorem, one may assert that the equation $f(x) = p$ has at most one solution x_0

in some small neighborhood of each point in D, for any $p \in \mathbb{R}^n$. In other words, $f(x)$ is locally univalent (1-1). The problem of global univalence (that is, univalence in all of D) can be expressed as follows:

(π_1) What additional properties of $f(x)$ guarantee that the equation $f(x) = p$ has at most one solution x_0 in D?

Certainly some such property of $f(x)$ is necessary as can be seen from the following

EXAMPLE 4-1. A mapping of $\mathbb{R}^2$ into itself, locally (1-1) but not globally (1-1). Set $f(x_1,x_2) = (x_1 \cos x_2, x_1 \sin x_2) = (f_1(x_1,x_2), f_2(x_1,x_2))$. The Jacobian determinant of f, $\det |J_f(x)| = x_1(\sin^2 x_2 + \cos^2 x_2) = x_1$. Thus f is locally (1-1) in any domain D in which $x_1 > 0$. However, $f(x_1,x_2) = f(x_1,x_2 + 2\pi)$. Thus f is certainly not globally (1-1) for any domain D containing points of the form (x_1,x_2), $(x_1,x_2 + 2\pi)$. Graphically we note that the mapping $f(x_1,x_2)$ bends a straight bar into an annulus.

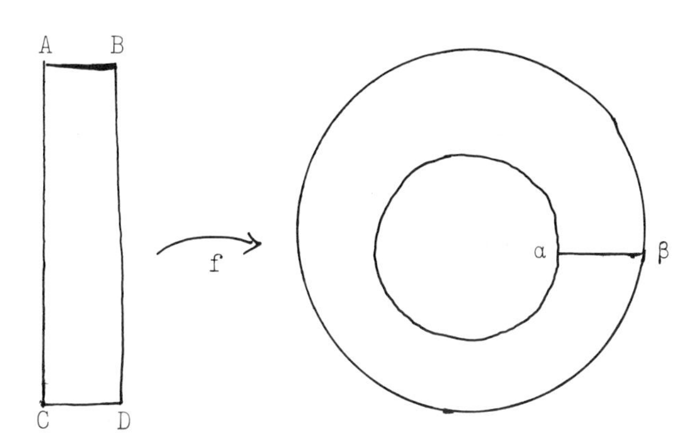

Figure 9. The mapping f bends the bar $ABCD$ into an annulus and $f(\overline{AB}) = f(\overline{CD}) = \overline{\alpha\beta}$.

It is interesting to note another formulation of global univalence which can be simply expressed as follows.

(π_2) What conditions on $f(x)$ insure that $d(f,p,D) = 1$?

The equivalence of (π_1) and (π_2) is proven quickly. Indeed as $\det|J_f(x)| > 0$,

$$d(f,p,D) = \sum_{f(x)=p} \operatorname{sgn} \det|J_f(x)|$$

$$= \text{number of solutions of } f(x) = p$$

Thus if $d(f,p,D) = 1$, $f(x) = p$ has exactly one solution.

To find conditions on $f(x)$ for global univalence let us first assume $f(x)$ is a gradient system, that is, $f(x) = \text{grad } F(x)$, where $F(x)$ is a C^2 real-valued function defined on D. Before proceding further we recall a definition and result from linear algebra. The principal minors of a square matrix A consist of all square submatrices of A whose principal diagonals lie along the principal diagonal of A. Then a result of Frobenius states that a real symmetric matrix A is positive definite if and only if all the principal minors of A have positive determinants. This fact is basic in the following

THEOREM 4-1. *Suppose* $f(x)$ *is a gradient system and all the principal minors of the Jacobian of* f *have positive determinants in some bounded convex domain* D, *then* $f(x)$ *is globally univalent*.

Proof. We need only show that if $f(x) = f(y)$ for $x, y \in D$, then $x = y$. This will surely follow for example if $f(x) = \text{grad } F(x)$ and $F(x)$ is a strictly convex function. For if $F(x)$ is strictly convex and $x \neq y$,

$F(x) + f(x)\cdot(y-x) < F(y)$ and $f(x) = f(y)$ would imply $x = y$. Now a necessary and sufficient condition that $F(x)$ be strictly convex in D is that the Hessian matrix $F_{x_i x_j}$ should be positive definite. Thus by the above result of Frobenius, $f(x)$ will be globally (1-1) if all the principal minor determinants of the matrix

$F_{x_i x_j} = J_f(x)$ are positive. Thus the theorem follows. ||

We now extend our global univalence theorem to mappings f that are not gradient systems. To this end recall that the symmetric part of any matrix A is defined to be $\frac{1}{2}(A + A^T)$, where A^T denotes the transpose of A.

THEOREM 4-2. *Let* f *be a continuously differentiable mapping of a bounded convex open set* D *in* $\mathbb{R}^n$ *into* $\mathbb{R}^n$. *Then* f *is globally univalent provided all the principal minor determinants of the symmetric part of the Jacobian of* f *are positive in* D.

Proof. Suppose $f = (f_1, f_2, \ldots, f_n)$, and let $x = (x_1, \ldots, x_n)$ and $a = (a_1, \ldots, a_n)$ be two distinct points in D. Set

$$\chi(t) = tx + (1-t)a, \quad \text{and}$$

$$\Phi(t) = (f(\chi(t)) - f(a)) \cdot (x-a)$$

As D is convex, $\chi(t) \in D$. Note that $\Phi(0) = 0$, and that $\Phi(1) \neq 0$ implies $f(x) \neq f(a)$. Now differentiating with respect to t, we obtain

$$\Phi'(t) = \sum_{i,j=1} \left(\frac{\partial f_i(\chi(t))}{\partial x_j}\right)(x_i - a_i)(x_j - a_j) \geq K|x-a|^2 \quad ||$$

By the result of Frobenius, under the hypothesis of the theorem, this quadratic form is positive definite. Thus

$\Phi'(t) > 0$ for $t \in (0, 1]$. By the Mean Value Theorem, $\Phi(1) = \Phi(0) + \Phi'(\theta) > 0$ with $0 < \theta < 1$. Thus $\Phi(1) > 0$ and $f(x) \neq f(a)$. Therefore f is univalent in D. ||

We now apply the idea of degree of a mapping mentioned in (π_2). We consider the case of a mapping $f(x)$ whose Jacobian determinant $\det J$ is positive in a convex domain D and the principal minor determinants of the symmetric part of J are merely nonnegative. To this end the following lemma is useful

LEMMA 4-3. _If the determinants of the principal minors of the symmetric part of the Jacobian of a function_ $f(x)$ _are nonnegative, then the determinants of the principal minors of the symmetric part of the Jacobian of_ $f(x) + \lambda x$ _are positive for_ $\lambda > 0$.

Proof. Denote the symmetric part of the Jacobian matrix of $f(x) + \lambda x$ by $J_\lambda^s = J^s + \lambda I$, where I is the identity matrix and J^s is the symmetric part of J. Then a principal minor of J_λ^s has the form $J_{\lambda,k}^s + \lambda I_k$, where $J_{\lambda,k}^s$ is a kth order principal minor of J_λ^s. Hence

$$\det|J_{\lambda,k}^s + \lambda I_k| = \lambda^k + g(\lambda)$$

where $g(\lambda)$ is a polynomial in λ of degree at most $k-1$ whose coefficients are sums of determinants of principal minors of $J^s_{\lambda,k}$. (This is a standard theorem of linear algebra concerning the characteristic polynomial of a square matrix.) Thus for $\lambda > 0$, $\det|J^s_{\lambda,k} + \lambda I_k| > 0$. ||

THEOREM 4-4. *Let* $f(x)$ *be a continuously differentiable mapping of a convex open bounded set* D *in* $\mathbb{R}^n$ *into* $\mathbb{R}^n$. *Suppose that the Jacobian determinant of* f *is positive in* D *and that the symmetric part of this Jacobian has non-negative principal minor determinants. Then* $f(x)$ *is univalent in* D.

Proof. Let a be an arbitrary point in D. We shall show that if $f(x) = f(a)$ for $x \in D$, then $x = a$. First note that by the hypotheses of the theorem the number of points x in D such that $f(x) = f(a)$ is finite. Indeed by the Implicit Function Theorem such points are isolated, and as $\overline{D}$ is bounded these points can have no limit point. Hence it suffices to prove the result for a subdomain in D' whose closure $\overline{D'} \subset D$ with $a \in \operatorname{int} D'$ and such that $f(x) \neq f(a)$ in $D - D'$. Thus $d(f, f(a), D')$ is defined, and by the equivalence of (π_1) and (π_2), it suffices to prove that this integer is $+1$. To accomplish this we consider the homotopy

$$H(x,t) = (1-t)[f(x) - f(a)] + t(x-a)$$

Clearly $H(x,1) = x-a$ and $d(H(x,1), 0, D') = 1$, thus $d(f, f(a), D') = 1$ provided $H(x,t) \neq 0$ for all $x \in \partial D'$ and $t \in (0, 1)$. If $H(x,t) = 0$ for some $x_0 \in \partial D'$ and t_0 a member of the open interval $(0, 1)$, then

$$(1-t_0)(f(x_0) - f(a)) + t_0(x_0-a) = 0$$

that is

$$g(x) \equiv f(x) - f(a) + \frac{t_0}{1-t_0}(x-a) = 0 \quad \text{at} \quad x = x_0$$

As $t_0/(1-t_0) > 0$, $g(x)$ has a positive Jacobian determinant, and by Lemma 4-3 the symmetric part of its Jacobian matrix has principal minors with positive determinants. Thus by Theorem 4-2, $g(x)$ is univalent in D. This contradicts the fact that $g(a) = g(x_0) = 0$ and $a, x_0 \in D$. Thus the homotopy $H(x,t) \neq 0$, and by the homotopy invariance of degree $d(f, f(a), D') = d(H(x,0), 0, D') = 1.$ ||

COROLLARY 4-5. <u>Let</u> $f(z) = u(x,y) + iv(x,y)$ <u>be defined and holomorphic in a bounded convex domain</u> D <u>of the</u> (x,y) <u>plane. If</u> $u_x \geq 0$ <u>in</u> D <u>and</u> $(u_x^2 + u_y^2) \neq 0$ <u>in</u> D, <u>then</u> $f(z)$ <u>is univalent in</u> D.

<u>Proof</u>. The Cauchy-Riemann equations imply (i) that the Jacobian determinant of $f(z)$, $\det|J_f(z)| = u_x^2 + u_y^2$; and

(ii) that the symmetric part of J_f, $J_f^s = u_x I$, where I is the identity matrix. The above theorem may therefore be applied to $f(z)$ in D, and yields the desired univalence. ||

Exercises

4-1. Let $f(z)$ be a holomorphic and univalent function defined on an open bounded set D in the complex plane. Prove that $f'(z) \neq 0$ in D. (For a generalization to functions of several complex variables see [1].)

4-2. Suppose $f(x,y) = (u(x,y), v(x,y))$ is a gradient system defined on a bounded convex domain D in $\mathbb{R}^2$. Prove that if $\det J_f(x) > 0$ and $u_x \geq 0$ on D, then f is globally univalent on D. Show, by example, that this conclusion may be false if $f(x,y)$ is not a gradient system.

4-3. Let $f(z) = (f_1(z),\ldots,f_n(z))$ be a holomorphic mapping defined on a convex bounded domain D in complex n-dimensional space $\mathbb{C}^n$. Here $z = (z_1,\ldots,z_n)$ and $f_i(z)$ $(i = 1,\ldots,n)$ is a holomorphic function of $z_1, z_2,\ldots,z_n$ (see Exercise 2-17). Prove that if the real part of the matrix $(\partial f_i/\partial z_j)$ is positive definite, then $f(z)$ is univalent in D.

4-4. Let $g(z) = (g_1(z),\ldots,g_n(z))$ be a globally univalent holomorphic mapping defined on a bounded domain D in $\mathbb{C}^n$. Prove that if

(i) $g(D)$ is convex and

(ii) the real part of the matrix $(\partial f_i/\partial z_j)(\partial g_i/\partial z_j)^{-1}$ is positive definite

and $f(z) = (f_1(z),\ldots,f_n(z))$ is a holomorphic mapping defined on D, then $f(z)$ is globally univalent on D.

§4-2. TOPICS IN NONLINEAR AUTONOMOUS ORDINARY DIFFERENTIAL EQUATIONS

We wish to describe the qualitative behavior of real solutions of the system

$$\frac{dx_i}{dt} = f_i(x_1, x_2,\ldots,x_n) \qquad (i = 1,\ldots,n) \qquad (4\text{-}1)$$

where $f_i(x_1, x_2,\ldots,x_n)$ are real-valued continuous functions. The well known existence theory for such systems shows that continuously differentiable solutions exist locally and are locally unique through any given point $x(\bar{t}) = (\bar{x}_1,\ldots,\bar{x}_n)$ provided the functions $f_i(x_1,\ldots,x_n)$ are Lipschitz continuous. These results do not give more precise qualitative information regarding the solutions. Such information can only be obtained by making further assumptions on the functions f_i.

1. Stationary Points. The simplest solutions of the system (4-1) are obtained by finding the real solutions $\tilde{x}$ of the system $f_i(x_1,\ldots,x_n) = 0$ $(i = 1,\ldots,n)$ and setting $x(t) = \tilde{x}$. Such solutions are called stationary points of the system (4-1).

A simple result that enables one to understand the significance of stationary points for the system (4-1) is the following lemma.

LEMMA 4-6. Let $x(t)$ be any solution of the system (4-1) such that $\lim_{t\to\infty} x(t) = b$, then provided $|b| < \infty$, b is a stationary point of (4-1).

Proof: Let $x(t) = (x_1, x_2, \ldots, x_n)$ and $b = (b_1, \ldots, b_n)$. If $\lim_{t\to\infty} x(t) = b$, for sufficiently large t either $x_i(t)$ is a monotonic function of t or the function $x_i(t)$ oscillates infinitely often about its limiting value b_i. In the first case, $0 = \lim_{t\to\infty}(dx_i(t)/dt) = \lim_{t\to\infty} f_i(x(t)) = f_i(b)$ as required. In the second case, by Rolle's Theorem $(dx_i(t)/dt) = f_i(x(t))$ vanishes infinitely often as $t \to \infty$ and as $\lim_{t\to\infty} f_i(x(t))$ exists $f_i(b) = 0$. ||

It is of interest to give information concerning the distribution of stationary points of the system (4-1). Such information can of course be obtained by the methods of Chapter 2 where the structure of the real solutions of systems of the form $f_i(x_1, \ldots, x_n) = 0$ $(i = 1, \ldots, n)$ was studied. For example if $\Sigma_{i=1}^{n} f_i x_i \neq 0$ on some sphere $\|x\| = R$, the system (4-1) has at least one stationary point insider the sphere $\|x\| = R$ (from the remarks in Section 2-6). Or if $\{f_i\}$ is a gradient system with grad $F = f$ and $F(x) \to \infty$ as $|x| \to \infty$, the system (4-1) always has at least one stationary point (from the problems of Section 2-3). Interesting estimates can be obtained for systems (4-1) defined on manifolds $\mathfrak{M}$ which are locally Euclidean. For example on a sphere S^{n-1}, for n odd, any system has at least two stationary points as follows from Theorem 2-20 of Hopf and the fact that the Euler-Poincaré characteristic of the sphere S^{n-1}, for odd n, $\chi(S^{n-1}) = 2$. On the other hand, by Theorems 2-37 and 2-41, if $\{f_i\}$ is a gradient system and the functions f_i are odd, the system has at least $2n$ stationary points.

2. Periodic Solutions for Plane Autonomous Systems.

Consider D any bounded open set in $\mathbb{R}^2$ and the system

$$\frac{dx_i}{dt} = f_i(x_1,x_2) \qquad (i = 1,2) \tag{4-2}$$

We suppose $f(x_1,x_2) = (f_1(x_1,x_2),\ f_2(x_1,x_2))$ is a continuous vector-valued mapping of $\mathbb{R}^2$ into itself vanishing only at isolated points in $\mathbb{R}^2$. Suppose also that this system has a unique continuous solution through any point $(x_0,y_0) \in \mathbb{R}^2$. Then we know the following facts about $d(f,0,D)$.

(i) $d(f,0,D) = 0$ if $\bar{D}$ contains no stationary points of the sytem (4-2).

(ii) For any nonvanishing continuous tangent vector field f, $d(f,0,D) = 1$ provided ∂D is the homeomorphic image of a circle, (that is, a Jordan curve).

These facts yield the following criteria for periodic solutions of systems in the form (4-2). A periodic orbit is a Jordan curve in the (x_1,x_2) plane which represents a periodic solution of the system (4-2).

THEOREM 4-7. *If* C *is a periodic orbit of the system* (4-2), *then* $d(f,0,\text{int } C) = 1$. *Thus a periodic orbit contains at least one critical point in its interior*.

Proof. C is a Jordan curve and f defines a system of tangent vectors to C. Since C does not pass through a stationary point of (4-2), by the uniqueness of solutions of system (4-2) made above, this tangent vector field is non-vanishing. Thus $d(f,0,\text{int } C) = 1$ by (ii) above. Hence by (i) above, the interior of C must contain at least one stationary point of (4-2). ||

COROLLARY 4-8. *The sum of the indices of the critical points in the interior of* C *must be* 1.

Proof. By the remarks at the end of Section 2-2, the degree is the sum of the indices. ||

3. *Behavior of Solutions near Isolated Stationary Points in the Plane.* The classical investigation of this case for $n = 2$ is due to Poincaré and Bendixson. One assumes that the stationary point occurs at $(0,0)$ and that the system (4-1) can be written

$$\frac{dx_1}{dt} = ax_1 + bx_2 + g_1(x_1,x_2)$$
$$\frac{dx_2}{dt} = cx_1 + dx_2 + g_2(x_1,x_2) \tag{4-3}$$

where a, b, c, d, are constants with $ad - bc \neq 0$ which guarantees that $(0,0)$ is an isolated stationary point and $g_1(x_1,x_2) = o(|x_1| + |x_2|)$ as $|x_1| + |x_2| \to 0$ for $(i = 1,2)$. Then for small $|x_1| + |x_2|$ one compares this system with the linearized system

$$\frac{dx_1}{dt} = ax_1 + bx_2$$
$$\frac{dx_2}{dt} = cx_1 + dx_2 \tag{4-4}$$

A basic result in this direction is the fact that if all solutions of the linearlized system (4-4) tend to the stationary point $(0,0)$ as $t \to \infty$ so do all solutions of the full nonlinear system (4-3). Similarly if every solution of (4-4) $\to \infty$ as $t \to \infty$, so does every solution of the nonlinear system. Furthermore the stationary point $(0,0)$ can be classified by the eigenvalues of the matrix $A = \begin{pmatrix} a & b \\ c & d \end{pmatrix}$, that is, one can show that the qualitative behavior of the nonlinear system near the critical point can be determined from the knowledge of the eigenvalues of A, except when the eigenvalues of A are pure imaginary. As the usual case is taken up in most texts on ordinary differential equations, we will study only the exceptional case. First let us consider the following example.

EXAMPLE 4-2. (<u>in which a knowledge of the eigenvalues of</u> A <u>does not predict the behavior of the nonlinear system</u>)

Consider

$$\frac{dx_1}{dt} = x_2 - x_1(x_1^2 + x_2^2) \tag{4-5}$$

$$\frac{dx_2}{dt} = -x_1 - x_2(x_1^2 + x_2^2) \tag{4-6}$$

The corresponding linear system has eigenvalues $\pm i$ and solutions $x_1(t) = c_1 \sin t + c_2 \cos t$ and $x_2(t) = c_1 \cos t - c_2 \sin t$; that is, periodic solutions. However for the nonlinear system, multiplying (4-5) by x_1, (4-6) by x_2, and adding, we obtain

$$x_1 \frac{dx_1}{dt} + x_2 \frac{dx_2}{dt} = -(x_1^2 + x_2^2)^2 \tag{4-7}$$

Thus setting $x_1 = r \cos \theta$ and $x_2 = r \sin \theta$ in (4-7), $r(dr/dt) = -r^4$. Integrating we obtain $(1/r)^2 = 2t + k$ where k is a constant. Consequently the nonlinear equations (4-5) and (4-6) can have no periodic solution, for if $t \to \infty$, $r \to 0$. Also if $t \to -k/2$, $r \to \infty$. Thus under no circumstances do solutions remain bounded away from infinity or the singular point $(0,0)$.

We now consider the so-called "problem of the center", for the system

$$\begin{aligned} \frac{dx_1}{dt} &= \beta x_2 + g_1(x_1,x_2) \\ \frac{dx_2}{dt} &= -\beta x_1 + g_2(x_1,x_2) \end{aligned} \tag{4-8}$$

that is, what conditions on $g_i(x_1,x_2)$ guarantee the existence of periodic solutions of the system (4-8) for $|x_1| + |x_2|$ sufficiently small. We shall obtain two results in this direction both of which can be generalized to n-dimensions. The first is a result of Poincaré.

THEOREM 4-9. _Suppose the functions_ $g_i(x_1,x_2)$ $(i = 1,2)$ _of_ (4-8) _satisfy the following symmetry conditions_ $g_1(x_1,-x_2) = -g_1(x_1,x_2)$ _and_ $g_2(x_1,-x_2) = g_2(x_1,x_2)$, _then all solutions_ $x(t) = (x_1(t), x_2(t))$ _of_ (4-8) _with_ $\beta \neq 0$ _and_ $|x(t)|$ _sufficiently small are periodic_. _Furthermore the orbits of these solutions encircle the origin_.

Proof. Assume β is negative (an analogous proof holds if β is positive). Consider any solution $x(t)$ beginning at the point $(x_1(0), x_2(0)) = (\bar{x},0)$ where $\bar{x} > 0$ is small. The symmetry conditions on g_1 and g_2 imply that such a trajectory is symmetric with respect to the x_1-axis so that

$x_1(t) = x_1(-t)$ and $x_2(t) = -x_2(-t)$. Since we are only interested in solutions with $|x(t)|$ very small, (dx_2/dx_1) can be computed approximately from the linearized equations, that is, $(dx_2/dx_1) = (dx_2/dt)(dx_1/dt) \simeq -(x_1/x_2)$. This means that x_2 and (dx_2/dx_1) have opposite signs provided $x_1 > 0$. Thus as t increases the trajectory $x(t)$ eventually crosses the x_2-axis and at that point $x_2 \neq 0$. Thereafter $x_1 < 0$, x and (dx_2/dx_1) have the same sign, and the magnitude of (dx_2/dx_1) is increasing. Hence for some $t_0 > 0$, $x_2(t_0) = 0$ and $x_1(t_0) < 0$, but then $x_1(t_0) = x_1(-t_0)$, $x_2(t_0) = -x_2(-t_0) = 0$; that is, the solution $x(t)$ is periodic. ||

Another quite distinct result in this direction is the following.

THEOREM 4-10. *Suppose* (4-8) *is a Hamiltonian system; that is,* $g_1 = (\partial N/\partial x_2)$ *and* $g_2 = -(\partial N/\partial x_1)$ *where* $N(x_1,x_2)$ *is a* C^2 *real-valued function of* (x_1,x_2) *with* $|\text{grad } N| < K(|x_1|^2 + |x_2|^2)$. *Then all solutions of* (4-8) *with* $|x(t)|$ *sufficiently small are periodic, and the orbits of these solutions encircle the origin*.

Proof. Set $H(x_1,x_2) = \frac{1}{2}\beta(x_1{}^2 + x_2{}^2) + N(x_1,x_2)$. Then (4-8) can be rewritten $(dx_1/dt) = (\partial H/\partial x_2)$.

$(dx_2/dt) = -(\partial H/\partial x_1)$. Now along any solution $(x_1(t),\ x_2(t))$ of (4-8),

$$\frac{dH}{dt} = \frac{\partial H}{\partial x_1}\frac{dx_1}{dt} + \frac{\partial H}{\partial x_2}\frac{dx_2}{dt} = \left(\frac{\partial H}{\partial x_1}\right)\left(\frac{\partial H}{\partial x_2}\right) - \left(\frac{\partial H}{\partial x_2}\right)\left(\frac{\partial H}{\partial x_1}\right) = 0$$

Thus $H(x_1(t),\ x_2(t)) = c$, a constant independent of t. By hypothesis c is sufficiently small, so that $H(x_1,x_2) = c$ defines a Jordan curve in the (x_1,x_2) plane (see Example 1-3). Thus any solution $(x_1(t),\ x_2(t))$ of (4-8) beginnning sufficiently close to the origin $(0,0)$ is periodic and defines a periodic orbit in the (x_1,x_2) plane enclosing the origin. For, by the argument used to prove Theorem 4-9 one notes that the trajectory $x(t)$, beginning at the point $(x_0,0)$ on the positive x_1-axis on $H(x_1,x_2) = c$, crosses the x_2-axis and can be continued uniquely so that $x(t)$ eventually returns to $(x_0,0)$. ||

4. Behavior of Solutions near Isolated Stationary Points in $\mathbb{R}^2$. We now consider the n-dimensional generalization of the last subsection. Suppose

$$\frac{dx}{dt} = Ax + f(x) \tag{4-9}$$

where A is a nonsingular constant matrix, $x(t) = (x_1(t),\ldots,x_n(t))$ is an n-vector of real-valued functions, and $f(x)$ is a continuously differentiable vector-valued function satisfying $|f(x)| = o(|x|)$ as $|x| \to 0$. With these assumptions the origin 0 is an isolated stationary point of (4-9), and we wish to find conditions that insure that the trajectories of the linearized system

$$\frac{dx}{dt} = Ax$$

provide qualitative information regarding the solutions of (4-9) near the origin. As one expects from the $\mathbb{R}^2$ case, the eigenvalues of A provide the desired information as long as the real parts of these numbers do not vanish. If some of the eigenvalues of A are pure imaginary the non-linear terms in $f(x)$ begin to have an influence and many fascinating phenomena occur.

Let us study a simple analogue of the problem of the center discussed in the last subsection. We consider the system

$$\frac{d^2x}{dt^2} + Ax + f(x) = 0 \tag{4-10}$$

where A is a positive definite self-adjoint matrix of constants, $x(t)$ is an n-vector of real-valued continuous functions, and $f(x)$ is a continuously differentiable vector-valued function of $x(t)$ with $|f(x)| = o(|x|)$ for $|x| \to 0$. The linearized problem

$$\frac{d^2x}{dt^2} + Ax = 0$$

then has all eigenvalues $\lambda_j^2 > 0$ $(j = 1,\ldots,n)$ and thus all solutions $x(t)$ are periodic, and the associated first order system

$$\frac{dx}{dt} = y$$

$$\frac{dy}{dt} = -Ax$$

has eigenvalues $\pm i\lambda_j$; in other words, all eigenvalues have zero real part.

THEOREM 4-11. _Suppose_ $f(x)$ _is a continuously differentiable gradient system; that is,_ $\operatorname{grad} F(x) = f(x)$ _where_ $F(x)$ _is a_ C^2 _real-valued function and_ $f(x) = o(|x|)$ _as_ $|x| \to 0$. _Then in the neighborhood of the origin_ (4-10) _has a family of periodic solutions_.

Sketch of Proof. This theorem is a consequence of the abstract result Theorem 3-15 if $F(x)$ is an even function. To demonstrate this fact a number of preliminary remarks are necessary. (The type of argument given below will recur in the next section and will be explained in greater detail there.)

(a) Set $t = \lambda s$. The equation (4-10) then becomes

$$\frac{d^2x}{ds^2} + \lambda^2[Ax + f(x)] = 0 \qquad (4\text{-}10')$$

Thus 2π-periodic solutions of (4-10') give rise to $2\pi\lambda$-periodic solutions of (4-10).

(b) A suitable Hilbert space H for the problem is defined as follows: Let W consist of all continuous, real-valued, 2π-periodic functions u with square integrable first derivatives, (denoted u') (see [2, page 165]). W is a Hilbert space with respect to the inner product $(u,v)_W = \int_0^{2\pi} uv + \int_0^{2\pi} u'v'$. Let $\tilde{H}$ be the direct sum of n copies of W. $\tilde{H}$ is also a Hilbert space with respect to the inner product $(u,v)_{\tilde{H}} = \Sigma_{i=1}^n (u_i,v_i)_W$ where $u = (u_1,\ldots,u_n)$, $v = (v_1,\ldots,v_n)$. A closed subspace of $\tilde{H}$, H, is defined as the set of all odd functions $u = (u_1,\ldots,u_n) \in \tilde{H}$. Thus H is a Hilbert space and a suitable inner product for two elements $u = (u_1,\ldots,u_n)$ and $v = (v_1,\ldots,v_n)$ of H is defined by

$$(u,v) = \sum_{i=1}^{n} \int_0^{2\pi} u_i'(s)v_i'(s)ds$$

This can be seen from the fact that if $u_i(s)$ is odd 2π-periodic and $\int_0^{2\pi} u_i(s)ds = 0$, then $\int_0^{2\pi} u_i^2 ds \leq \int_0^{2\pi} (u_i')^2 ds$. (See [3, page 185].)

(c) By a generalized 2π- periodic solution of (4-10') we mean a function $x(s) = (x_1(s),\ldots,x_n(s)) \in H$ such that

$$\int_0^{2\pi} x'(s) \cdot v'(s)ds = \lambda^2\{\int_0^{2\pi} [Ax\cdot v]ds + \int_0^{2\pi} [f(x)\cdot v]ds \quad (4\text{-}10'')$$

holds for all functions $v(s) \in H$. Although we shall not do so here, it can be shown that generalized 2π-periodic solutions of (4-10") are <u>smooth</u> 2π-periodic solutions of (4-10").

(d) Each integral in (4-10") is a linear functional of v, and each functional can be shown to be bounded in H. Thus by the Riesz Representation Theorem for linear functionals on the Hilbert space H we may rewrite (4-10") as

$$(x - \lambda^2 Lx - \lambda^2 Nx, v) = 0 \qquad (4\text{-}10''')$$

where $(x,v) = \int_0^{2\pi} x'\cdot v'ds$, $(Lx,v) = \int_0^{2\pi} Ax\cdot vds$, $(Nx,v) = \int_0^{2\pi} f(x)\cdot vds$. Thus, as v is arbitrary, (4.10"') is equivalent to $x = \lambda^2[Lx + Nx]$.

Now we are in a position to apply the abstract Theorem 3-15. Indeed we see that existence of periodic solutions is related to the investigation of the operator equation $x = \lambda^2[Lx + Nx]$ in the space H. To apply Theorem 3-15 we need only verify the following properties:

(i) L and N are completely continuous operators

(ii) L is positive definite and self-adjoint, and N is a gradient operator

(iii) $((L + N)x, x) > 0$ for $x \neq 0$ and $\|x\|$ sufficiently small.

(i) follows from the fact that A is a positive definite, self-adjoint matrix and $\operatorname{grad} F = f(x)$. Indeed

$$(Lx,v) = \int_0^{2\pi} A\mathbf{x}\cdot v\,ds = \int_0^{2\pi} x\cdot Av\,ds = (x,Lv) \quad \text{and}$$

$$(Lx,x) = \int_0^{2\pi} Ax\cdot x\,ds > 0$$

Similarly the gradient of the functional $\int_0^{2\pi} F(x)ds$ in H is Nx, as $(Nx,v) = \int_0^{2\pi} f(x)\cdot v\,ds$.

(ii) follows from the following property of the function space H (see Appendix II). If $x_m \to x$ weakly in H (that is, each component $x_m^{(i)} \to x^{(i)}$ $(i = 1,\ldots,n)$ weakly in W), then $x_m^{(i)} \to x^{(i)}$ strongly in $L_2[0,2\pi]$ and $C[0,2\pi]$ for $(i = 1,\ldots,n)$. Thus if $x_m \to x$ weakly in H

$$\|Lx_m - Lx\|_H = \sup_{\|v\|=1} (L(x_m-x),v) = \sup_{\|v\|=1} \int_0^{2\pi} A(x_m-x)\cdot v\,ds$$

$$= \sup_{\|v\|=1} \int_0^{2\pi} (x_m-x)\cdot Av\,ds$$

$$\leq \sum_{i=1}^{n} K\|x_m^{(i)} - x^{(i)}\|_{L_2[0,2\pi]}$$

by Schwarz's inequality, where K is a constant independent of x_m. So that as $m \to \infty$, $Lx_m \to Lx$ strongly in H. Similarly, (denoting the $L_2[0,2\pi]$ norm by $\| \|_{0,2}$)

$$\|Nx_m - Nx\|_H = \sup_{\|v\|=1} \int_0^{2\pi} (f(x_m) - f(x))\cdot v \, ds$$

$$\leq \sum_{i=1}^{n} K\|f^i(x_m) - f^i(x)\|_{0,2}$$

by Schwarz's inequality, where K is a constant independent of x_m. Furthermore, by the Mean Value Theorem, for $\theta_m^{(i)}$ on the line segment joining x and x_m

$$\|Nx_m - Nx\|_H \leq \sum_{i=1}^{n} K\|(\text{grad } f^i(\theta_m^{(i)}))\cdot(x_m - x)\|_{0,2}$$

$$\leq \sum_{i=1}^{n} K\|\text{grad } f^i(\theta_m^{(i)})\|_{0,2}\|x_m - x\|_{0,2}$$

by Schwarz's inequality. As $|x_m|$ and $|x|$ are uniformly bounded on $[0,2\pi]$, $\|(\text{grad } f^i(\theta_m^{(i)})\|_{0,2}$ is uniformly bounded, by M say,

$$\|Nx_m - Nx\|_H \leq \sum_{i=1}^{n} KM\|x_m^{(i)} - x^{(i)}\|_{0,2}$$

Therefore as $m \to \infty$, $Nx_m \to Nx$ strongly in H.

(iii) Finally we show that $(Lx + Nx, x) > 0$ for $\|x\|$ sufficiently small and nonzero. Indeed

$$(Lx + Nx, x) = \int_0^{2\pi} [Ax\cdot x + f(x)\cdot x] ds$$

As A is a positive definite matrix and $|f(x)| = o(|x|)$, there are positive constants K and $\epsilon(|x|)$ with $\epsilon(|x|) \to 0$ as $|x| \to 0$ such that $Ax \cdot x \geq K|x|^2$ and $|f(x)| \leq \epsilon(|x|)|x|$. Hence

$$(Lx + Nx, x) \geq \int_0^{2\pi} [K|x|^2 - \epsilon(|x|)|x|^2]ds$$

$$\geq \int_0^{2\pi} [K - \epsilon(|x|)]|x|^2 ds$$

Therefore for $\|x\|$ sufficiently small, $|x|^2$ is so small that $(K - \epsilon(|x|)) > 0$; so that $(Lx + Nx, x) = 0$ implies $\int_0^{2\pi} |x|^2 ds = 0$, that is, $x \equiv 0$.

Thus, by Theorem 3-15, for each real number c with $0 < c \leq c_0$ (c_0 sufficiently small), there is a solution x_c of the equation $x = \lambda_c(Lx + Nx)$ with $\|x_c\| = c$. These solutions correspond to a family of periodic solutions of (4-10). (Note that this family is nontrivial in the sense that $x_c \not\equiv x(t + c)$ since the H-norms of x_c all differ.)

In case $F(x)$ is not even, a similar proof can be given by studying the operator equation associated to (4.10') in the Hilbert space $\tilde{H}$ itself. Instead of relying on Theorem 3-15, a direct proof can be given by showing that the variational problem $\min_{\partial B_c} \int_0^{2\pi} \dot{x}^2$ where $\partial B_c = \{x \mid x \in \tilde{H}, \int_0^{2\pi} [Ax \cdot x + 2F(x)] = 2c\}$ for c sufficiently small determines a family of critical points x_c which

correspond to a family of distinct periodic solutions of (4-10
in the neighborhood of the origin.

Exercises

4-5. Consider the system $x_i' = f_i(x_1,x_2)$ $(i = 1,2)$. Suppose $f_i(x_1,x_2)$ is 2π-periodic and smooth in x_1 and x_2. Prove

(i) the system can be considered as a differential equation on a torus

(ii) if $f_1^2 + f_2^2 > 0$ for $x,y \in ([0,2\pi] \times [0,2\pi])$, then the system has no singular points on the torus

(iii) if the system is Hamiltonian (that is; $f_1 = \partial u/\partial x_1$) then there are at least 3 singular points on the torus.

4-6. (An example of Volterra from biology) Prove the system

$$x' = x - xy$$

$$y' = -y + xy$$

has periodic solutions with a center at the point $(1,1)$. Compare the system with its linearization. (Hint: Show that along any solution $x + y - \log x - \log y = \text{constant}$, and examine the shape of this curve near $(1,1)$.)

4-7. (An example of Poincare on the motion of the moon) Prove the system

$$r' = M(r \cos \theta, r \sin \theta)[1 + \alpha r^2 + \beta r^4] \sin \theta$$

$$\theta' = (1 + re^2) + r^{-1}M(1 + \delta e^2) \cos \theta$$

has periodic solutions near the origin, where $M(x,y)$ is an even function of (x,y) and $M(x,y) = O(x^2 + y^2)$. (Hint: Set $x = r \cos \theta$ and $y = r \sin \theta$ and apply Theorem 4-9.)

4-8. Prove, by example, that Theorem 4-11 need not hold if $f(x)$ is not a gradient. (Hint: Show that the system

$$x_1'' + x_1 + x_2(x_1^2 + x_2^2) = 0$$

$$x_2'' + x_2 - x_1(x_1^2 + x_2^2) = 0$$

has no periodic solution other than $x(t) \equiv 0$.)

4-9. Investigate the periodic solutions of each of the equations

(i) $x'' + x + x^2 = 0$

(ii) $x'' + x + x^3 = 0$.

4-10. Show that the period of the solutions constructed in Theorem 4-11 in a small neighborhood of the origin is near the smallest nonzero period of the solutions of the linear system $x'' + Ax = 0$.

§4-3. TOPICS IN ELLIPTIC PARTIAL DIFFERENTIAL EQUATIONS

The results obtained on infinite dimensional systems in Chapter 3 have interesting consequences in the theory of partial differential equations. For simplicity we shall limit ourselves to that class of problems known as elliptic boundary-value problems, which are the higher dimensional analogues of the boundary-value problems for ordinary differential equations.

Let us begin by considering two very special but histori-cally significant problems. Throughout this section G is a bounded domain in $\mathbb{R}^n$ with boundary ∂G and $x = (x_1, x_2, \ldots, x_n)$ denotes a general point of G. We consider the Laplace operator $\Delta = \Sigma_{i=1}^n \partial^2/\partial x_i^2$ defined over G.

<u>Problem 1</u> <u>The linear Dirichlet problem</u>. Suppose that $g(x)$ is a function defined on G. Find a real-valued function $u(x)$ defined on $\bar{G}$ satisfying

$$\Delta u = g(x) \quad \text{on } G$$
$$u = 0 \quad \text{on } \partial G$$

<u>Problem 2</u> <u>The linear eigenvalue problem</u>. Find all real numbers λ and real-valued functions $u(x)$ $(\not\equiv 0)$ such that

$$\Delta u + \lambda u = 0 \quad \text{on } G$$
$$u = 0 \quad \text{on } \partial G$$

The Laplace operator Δ and the Dirichlet problem are the classic examples of elliptic operators and elliptic boundary value problems, respectively.

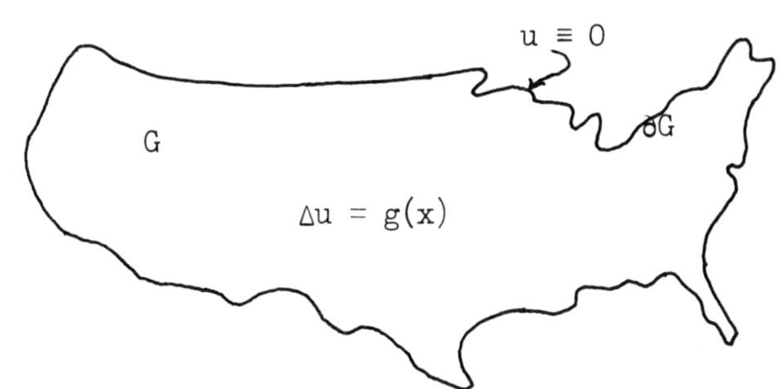

Figure 10. Illustrating the linear Dirichlet Problem.

A well-known reformulation of Problems 1 and 2 is to assign to each problem a so-called Green's function $K(x,y)$: where $K(x,y)$ satisfies

$$\Delta K(x,y) = \delta(x-y) \quad \text{for} \quad x \in G$$
$$K(x,y) = 0 \quad \text{for} \quad x \in \partial G$$

and for all $y \in G$. Here $\delta(x-y)$ denotes the Dirac delta function. Then Problems 1 and 2 can be written as integral equations as follows:

<u>For Problem 1</u> $\qquad u(x) = \int_G K(x,y)g(y)dy$

<u>For Problem 2</u> $\qquad u(x) = \lambda\int_G K(x,y)u(y)dy$

If we denote by $C_0(\overline{G})$ the Banach space of continuous functions $u(x)$ defined on $\overline{G}$, vanishing on ∂G, with norm $\|u(x)\| = \sup_G |u(x)|$, then it can be demonstrated that the linear mapping $Lf(y) = \int_G K(x,y)f(y)dy$ is a compact mapping of $C_0(\overline{G})$ (the set of continuous functions on $\overline{G}$, vanishing on ∂G) into itself. Thus by the Approximation Lemma 3-4, Problems 1 and 2 can be thoroughly studied by finite dimensional linear approximations, (provided $g(x)$ and ∂G are sufficiently smooth).

Should the function $g(x)$ of Problem 1 be continuous but not necessarily Lipschitz continuous, then the associated Dirichlet Problem might not be solvable in the usual sense [4, page 246]. Hence some other viewpoint is necessary.

Another approach to both Problems 1 and 2 is to divide each problem into two parts: an existence part, in which one proves that the problem has a solution in some "averaged" sense; and a regularity part, in which the above solution is proved to be sufficiently smooth, that is, to satisfy the equation at each point of G and the boundary condition. In order to settle the existence part of Problems 1 and 2 we define so-called weak solutions of both problems. These solutions are defined by means of the Dirichlet form

$$D[u,v] = \sum_{i=1}^{n} \int_G u_{x_i} v_{x_i}$$

associated with the Laplace operator Δu.

These averaged or "generalized" solutions are not necessarily differentiable in the classical sense. However they can be regarded as limits of differentiable functions in the following sense:

DEFINITION 4-12. *A function* $u(x) \in L_2(G)$ *possesses a square integrable generalized partial derivative* u_{x_i} *if there is a sequence of continuously differentiable functions* $u_n(x)$ *such that* $u_n(x) \to u(x)$ *and* $(u_n(x))_{x_i} \to u_{x_i}$ *in* $L_2(G)$. (*Note that the generalized derivative is unique (apart from a set of measure zero) if it exists*.)

The totality of functions $u(x) \in L_2(G)$ all of whose first order generalized partial derivatives are square integrable forms a linear space which we call $W_{1,2}(G)$. We make $W_{1,2}(G)$ into a Hilbert space by defining the inner product

$$(u,v)_{1,2} = \int_G uv + D[u,v]$$

The set of infinitely differentiable functions vanishing outside a compact subset of G is denoted $C_0^\infty(G)$; clearly $C_0^\infty(G) \subset W_{1,2}(G)$. The closure of these functions in $W_{1,2}(G)$ forms a closed linear subspace which we denote by $\dot{W}_{1,2}(G)$.

The reader is referred to [5] for further remarks on generalized differentiation and the so-called Sobolev spaces $\dot{W}_{1,2}(G)$.

DEFINITION 4-13. *A generalized solution of Problem 1 is a function* $u(x) \in \dot{W}_{1,2}(G)$ *such that*

$$D[u,\phi] + \int_G g(x)\phi = 0$$

for all functions $\phi \in \dot{W}_{1,2}(G)$.

DEFINITION 4-14. *A generalized solution of Problem 2 is a function* $u(x) \in \dot{W}_{1,2}(G)$ *such that* $\int_G u^2 = 1$ *and satisfyi*

$$D[u,\phi] = \lambda \int_G u(x)\phi$$

for some fixed λ *and all* $\phi \in \dot{W}_{1,2}(G)$.

The term "generalized" solution is justified by the following result.

LEMMA 4-15. *Smooth solutions of Problems 1 and 2 are generalized solutions.*

Proof. Suppose $u(x)$ is a twice continuously differentiabl solution of Problem 1. Let $\phi \in \dot{W}_{1,2}(G)$. Then multiplying

$$\phi\Delta u = g(x)\phi$$

and integrating over G

$$\int_G \phi\Delta u = \int_G g(x)\phi$$

Integrating by parts and using the fact that u vanishes on ∂G we obtain

$$D[u,\phi] = -\int_G g(x)\phi$$

Thus u is a generalized solution of Problem 1 as u is automatically an element of $\dot{W}_{1,2}(G)$.

The proof for Problem 2 is analogous. ||

The converse of this lemma is the regularity part of the Dirichlet problem mentioned above. The interested reader can find a complete discussion of regularity in the monograph of Agmon [5].

For the remainder of this section the following notation and basic results will be used. The norm of an element $u \in \dot{W}_{1,2}(G)$ will be denoted $\|u\|_{1,2}$. If $v \in L_2(G)$ its norm is denoted $\|v\|_{0,2}$. Thus $\|u\|_{1,2}^2 = D[u] + \|u\|_{0,2}^2$, where $D[u] = D[u,u]$. Henceforth all inner products refer to $\dot{W}_{1,2}(G)$, and we shall denote them simply by $(\ ,\ )$. Furthermore, as G is a bounded domain in $\mathbb{R}^n$, the following facts (see [5]) will be used:

(a) (Poincaré's Inequality) For any $u \in \dot{W}_{1,2}(G)$, $\|u\|_{0,2}^2 \leq KD[u]$, where K is a positive constant independent of u.

(b) For any $u \in \dot{W}_{1,2}(G)$, $D[u] = 0$ if and only if $u \equiv 0$.

(c) (Rellich's lemma) If $u_n \to u$ weakly in $\dot{W}_{1,2}(G)$, then $u_n \to u$ strongly in $L_2(G)$.

THEOREM 4-16. <u>If</u> $g(x) \in L_2(G)$, <u>the generalized solution of Problem 1 exists and is unique</u>.

<u>Proof</u>. First we show that the generalized solutions of Problem 1 can be identified with the solutions of an operator equation $Lu = f$ in $\dot{W}_{1,2}(G)$. This equation is obtained as follows: $D[u,\phi]$ is a continuous bilinear functional in ϕ and u on the Hilbert space $\dot{W}_{1,2}(G)$. Thus by a standard result in Hilbert space theory, $D[u,\phi] = (Lu,\phi)_{1,2}$ where L is a continuous linear mapping of $\dot{W}_{1,2}(G)$ into itself. Also, $\int_G g(x)\phi$ is a linear functional in ϕ defined on $\dot{W}_{1,2}(G)$. As $g(x) \in L_2(G)$, this functional is continuous. Indeed, let $\phi_n \to \phi$ strongly in $\dot{W}_{1,2}(G)$, then

$$|\int_G g(x)(\phi-\phi_n)| \leq \|g\|_{0,2}\|\phi-\phi_n\|_{0,2} \leq \|g\|_{0,2}\|\phi-\phi_n\|_{1,2}$$

Thus $\int_G g\phi_n \to \int_G g\phi$. Consequently by the Riesz Representation Theorem, $\int_G g\phi = -(f,\phi)_{1,2}$ where $f \in \dot{W}_{1,2}(G)$. Thus if u is a generalized solution of Problem 1,

$$D[u,\phi] + \int_G g\phi = (Lu - f, \phi) = 0$$

for all $\phi \in \dot{W}_{1,2}(G)$. Hence $Lu = f$. Conversely, if $u \in \dot{W}_{1,2}(G)$ and satisfies $Lu = f$, then u is a generalized solution of Problem 1.

The second step then proceeds by noting that

$Lu = \text{grad}(\frac{1}{2}D[u])$ and $D[u]$ is weakly lower semi-continuous by Corollary 3-13 of Theorem 3-12 of Section 3-3. This theorem guarantees then that $Lu = f$ has a solution in $\dot{W}_{1,2}(G)$ provided $D[u]/\|u\| \to \infty$ as $\|u\| \to \infty$. That this last proviso holds can be seen as follows. By Poinicaré's inequality

$$\|u\|_{0,2}^2 \leq KD[u]$$

Thus

$$\|u\|_{1,2}^2 = D[u] + \|u\|_{0,2}^2 \leq (1+K)D[u]$$

and

$$\frac{D[u]}{\|u\|_{1,2}} \geq \frac{1}{1+K} \|u\|_{1,2} \to \infty \text{ as } \|u\|_{1,2} \to \infty$$

Finally, to prove uniqueness, we note that if u and v are generalized solutions of Problem 1, the difference $w = u-v$ satisfies $D[w,\phi] = 0$ for all $\phi \in \dot{W}_{1,2}(G)$. In particular, setting $\phi = w$, we have $D[w,w] = D[w] = 0$. Thus $w = 0$, that is $u = v$. ||

THEOREM 4-17. Problem 2 has a countably infinite number of distinct generalized solutions u_n with associated eigenvalues $\lambda_n \to \infty$.

Proof. The existence of one solution u_1 with

$\int_G u_1^2 = 1$ is a consequence of Theorem 3-15 of Section 3-3. The proof is carried out exactly as in Theorem 4-16 by translating the problem into the question of solvability of an operator equation in the Hilbert space $\dot{W}_{1,2}(G)$. In this case, we show the complete continuity of the operator $\mathcal{L}u$ defined by

$$(\mathcal{L}u, \phi) = \int_G u\phi$$

for all $\phi \in \dot{W}_{1,2}(G)$. To this end let $u_n \to u$ weakly in $\dot{W}_{1,2}(G)$, then

$$\begin{aligned} \|\mathcal{L}u_n - \mathcal{L}u\| &= \sup_{\|\phi\|=1} (\mathcal{L}u_n - \mathcal{L}u, \phi) \\ &= \sup_{\|\phi\|=1} \int_G (u_n - u)\phi \\ &\leq K\|u_n - u\|_{0,2}\,, \end{aligned}$$

where K is a constar independent of u_n.

Now by Rellich's lemma, $u_n \to u$ strongly in $L_2(G)$, thus $\mathcal{L}u_n \to \mathcal{L}u$ and $\mathcal{L}u$ is a completely continuous mapping. Furthermore, the reader will verify that $\mathcal{L}u$ is the gradier of the functional $\frac{1}{2}\int_G u^2$ in $\dot{W}_{1,2}(G)$.

The linearity of Problem 2 can then be used to define a sequence of solutions $u_2, u_3, \ldots$ by applying the above mentioned Theorem 3-15 successively to the Hilbert spaces obtained by taking the orthogonal complement of u_1 in

$\dot{W}_{1,2}(G)$, the orthogonal complement of the subspace formed by the vectors u_1, u_2 in $\dot{W}_{1,2}(G)$ respectively,.... The proof of Lemma 3-18 of Section 3-5 insures that the countably infinite number of distinct solutions so constructed are associated with eigenvalues $\lambda_n \to \infty$. ||

We now turn to the simplest nonlinear analogues of the Problems 1 and 2.

<u>Problem 1'</u> <u>A nonlinear Dirichlet problem</u>. Find a real-valued function $u(x)$ defined on $\bar{G}$ satisfying

$$\Delta u = f(x,u,u_x) \quad \text{on } G$$
$$u = 0 \quad \text{on } \partial G$$

where u_x denotes the n-vector $(u_{x_1}, u_{x_2},\ldots,u_{x_n})$

<u>Problem 2'</u> <u>A nonlinear eigenvalue problem</u>. Find a real number $\lambda (\neq 0)$ and a real-valued function $u(x)$ $(\not\equiv 0)$ defined on $\bar{G}$ satisfying

$$\Delta u + \lambda g(u,u_x) = 0 \quad \text{on } G$$
$$u = 0 \quad \text{on } \partial G$$

(Here we assume $g(0,0) = 0$, so that $u(x) \equiv 0$ is a solution of the problem for all λ.)

Of course these problems may have no solutions unless we impose certain conditions on the functions $f(x,u,u_x)$ and

$g(u,u_x)$ (see Exercise 4-11). One such condition is known to be growth restrictions on the functions f and g as $|u|$ and $|u_x| \to \infty$. Such restrictions were carefully studied by S. Bernstein - in the early part of this century. Furthermore we shall assume that $g(u,u_x) = g(u)$ is independent of u_x. These conditions are expressed in the theorems below by means of the boundedness and continuity properties of operators associated with f and g.

DEFINITION 4-18. _A generalized solution of Problem 1' is a function_ $u(x) \in \dot{W}_{1,2}(G)$ _satisfying_

$$D[u,\phi] = -\int_G f(x,u,u_x)\phi$$

for all $\phi \in \dot{W}_{1,2}(G)$.

DEFINITION 4-19. _A generalized solution of Problem 2' is a function_ $u(x) \in \dot{W}_{1,2}(G)$ _such that_ $D[u] \neq 0$ _and satisfying_

$$D[u,\phi] = \lambda \int_G g(u)\phi$$

for all $\phi \in \dot{W}_{1,2}(G)$.

As in Lemma 4-15, smooth solutions of Problems 1' and 2' are generalized solutions.

THEOREM 4-20. Problem 1' always has a unique generalized solution provided (i) $f(x,0,0) \in L_2(G)$, (ii) the integral

$$\int_G [f(x,u,u_x) - f(x,v,v_x)][u-v]$$

exists and is nonnegative for all $u, v \in \dot{W}_{1,2}(G)$, and (iii) the operator B defined by $(Bu,\phi)_{1,2} = \int_G f(x,u,u_x)\phi$ is continuous and bounded in $\dot{W}_{1,2}(G)$.

Proof. This theorem follows from Theorem 3-10 of Section 3-2 and its corollary for $u, \phi \in \dot{W}_{1,2}(G)$. Indeed $\int_G f(x,u,u_x)\phi$ is a linear functional in ϕ on $\dot{W}_{1,2}(G)$. Thus by the Riesz Representation Theorem (Appendix II) and hypothesis (iii), the operator B maps $\dot{W}_{1,2}(G)$ into itself. Furthermore

$$D[u,\phi] + \int_G f(x,u,u_x)\phi = 0$$

can be written $Lu + Bu = 0$ in the Hilbert space $\dot{W}_{1,2}(G)$, as in the proof of Theorem 4-16. Hypothesis (ii) above implies $Tu \equiv Lu + Bu$ is a monotone mapping, that is $(Tu-Tv, u-v) \geq 0$ $(u \neq v)$. Furthermore

$$\frac{(Tu,u)}{\|u\|} \to \infty \quad \text{as} \quad \|u\| \to \infty$$

Indeed,

$$(Tu,u) = (Lu,u) + (Bu,u) = D[u] + \int_G f(x,u,u_x)u$$

$$\geq D[u] + \int_D f(x,0,0)u \quad \text{(by hypothesis (ii))}$$

$$\geq D[u] - \|f(x,0,0\|_{0,2}\|u\|_{0,2} \quad \text{(By Cauchy-Schwarz inequality).}$$

Therefore

$$\frac{(Tu,u)}{\|u\|_{1,2}} \geq \frac{D[u]}{\|u\|_{1,2}} \frac{\|f(x,0,0\|_{0,2}\|u\|_{0,2}}{\|u\|_{1,2}}$$

$$\geq \frac{1}{(1+K)} \|u\|_{1,2} - \tilde{K} \qquad \text{(by hypothesis (i))}$$

where K and $\tilde{K}$ are positive constants independent of $\|u\|_{1,2}$. Therefore as $\|u\|_{1,2} \to \infty$, $(Tu,u)/\|u\|_{1,2} \to \infty$. Now the desired conclusion follows by hypothesis (iii) since B is a continuous and bounded operator. ||

What growth restrictions on $f(x,u,u_x)$ insure that B is a bounded and continuous operator? For simplicity, we shall be content with the rather stringent condition of global Lipschitz continuity of f, namely we shall assume

$$|f(x,s,t_1,\ldots,t_n) - f(x,s',t_1',\ldots,t_n')| \leq K[|s-s'| + \sum_{i=1}^{n} |t_i-t_i'|] \qquad \text{(L)}$$

where K is a positive constant independent of x, s, t_i, s', t_i'. (These restrictions can be substantially lightened by a careful study of the so-called Sobolev inequalities.)

LEMMA 4-21. *If* $f(x,u,u_x)$ *satisfies hypothesis* (L), *the operator* B *is a continuous and bounded mapping of* $\dot{W}_{1,2}(G)$ *into itself*.

Proof. Suppose $u_n \to u$ strongly in $\dot{W}_{1,2}(G)$. Then

$$\|Bu_n - Bu\| = \sup_{\|\phi\|=1} (Bu_n - Bu, \phi)$$

$$= \sup_{\|\phi\|=1} \int_G [f(x,u_n,(u_n)_x) - f(x,u,u_x)]\phi$$

Thus by the Cauchy-Schwarz inequality and hypothesis (L)

$$\|Bu_n - Bu\| \leq \int_G [f(x,u_n,(u_n)_x - f(x,u,u_x)]^2$$

$$\leq K^2 \int_G [(u_n - u)^2 + \text{grad}(u-u_n)\cdot\text{grad}(u-u_n)]$$

$$\leq K^2\|u - u_n\|^2_{1,2}$$

Thus as $n \to \infty$, $Bu_n \to Bu$ and B is therefore a continuous operator.

To show that B is bounded (that is, B maps bounded sets into bounded sets), suppose $\|u\|_{1,2} \leq M$. As $\|Bu\| \leq \|B(0)\| + \|Bu - B(0)\|$, by the Lipschitz continuity of $f(x,u,u_x)$

$$\|Bu - B(0)\| = \sup_{\|\phi\|=1} (Bu - B(0), \phi)$$
$$\leq \|f(x,u,u_x) - f(x,0,0)\|_{0,2}$$
$$\leq K[\|u\|^2_{0,2} + \|u_x\|^2_{0,2}]^{\frac{1}{2}}$$
$$\leq KM$$

Thus $\|Bu\| \leq \|B(0)\| + KM$. So B is a bounded operator, and this completes the proof. ||

THEOREM 4-22. Suppose (i) $xg(x) > 0$ for $x \neq 0$ and (ii) the operator B defined by $(Bu,\phi) = \int_G g(u)\phi$ is a completely continuous operator for $\phi, u \in \dot{W}_{1,2}(G)$. Then the nonlinear eigenvalue Problem 2' has a one parameter family of non-identically zero generalized solutions $u_c(x)$ with $D[u_c] = c$.

Proof. This result follows immediately from Theorem 3-15, the last theorem in Section 3-3, by noting that the generalized solutions of Problem 2' can be identified with the solutions of the operator equation

$$\text{grad } F(u) = \lambda \text{ grad } G(u)$$

in $\dot{W}_{1,2}(G)$, where $F(u) = D[u]$ and $G(u) = \int_0^1 ug(su)ds$. ||

Again we might ask what growth condition on $g(u)$ guarantees that the operator B is completely continuous.

As in Lemma 4-21, global Lipschitz continuity suffices, as the following result shows. (We note once more that this condition can be considerably lightened by a careful use of the Sobolev imbedding theorems. A statement of these theorems is given in [2].)

LEMMA 4-23. *If* $|g(x) - g(y)| \leq C|x - y|$, *where* C *is a positive constant independent of* x, y, *then* B *is a completely continuous mapping.*

Proof. Let $u_n \to u$ weakly in $\dot{W}_{1,2}(G)$, then

$$\begin{aligned}
\|Bu_n - Bu\| &= \sup_{\|\phi\|=1} (Bu_n - Bu, \phi) \\
&= \sup_{\|\phi\|=1} \int_G (g(u_n) - g(u))\phi \\
&\leq K\|g(u_n) - g(u)\|_{0,2} \\
&\leq \bar{C}\|u_n - u\|_{0,2}
\end{aligned}$$

Thus by Rellich's lemma, $\|u_n - u\|_{0,2} \to 0$ as $n \to \infty$ and $Bu_n \to Bu$ strongly, that is, B is a completely continuous mapping. $\|$

Thus far we have been concerned with partial differential equations whose leading term has always been the Laplace operator. We shall end our discussion of elliptic boundary-value problems by demonstrating that generalized solutions can be defined for much more complicated equations.

First some notation and definitions. Elementary differential operators $\partial/\partial x_j$ defined on G will be denoted D_j, and for any n-tuple of nonnegative integers $\alpha = (\alpha_1, \alpha_2, \ldots, \alpha_n)$ the corresponding differential operator $\partial^\alpha/\partial x_1^{\alpha_1} \partial x_2^{\alpha_2} \ldots \partial x_n^{\alpha_n}$ is written $D^\alpha = D_1^{\alpha_1} D_2^{\alpha_2} \ldots D_n^{\alpha_n}$. The order of the operator D^α is defined to be $|\alpha| = \alpha_1 + \alpha_2 + \ldots + \alpha_n$. A general real linear differential operator L of order m defined on G is then written concisely as

$$Lu = \sum_{|\alpha| \leq m} a_\alpha(x) D^\alpha u$$

where $a_\alpha(x)$ are real-valued functions defined on G.

A differential operator A of order $2m$ (not necessarily linear) is called a divergence expression of order m if it can be written

$$Au = \sum_{|\alpha| \leq m} D^\alpha A_\alpha(x, u, \ldots, D^m u)$$

where the functions A_α are sufficiently smooth. In that case we associate with the operator A the Dirichlet form

$$a(u,v) = \sum_{|\alpha| \leq m} \int_G (-1)^{|\alpha|} A_\alpha(x, u, \ldots, D^m u) D^\alpha v$$

One then defines a function $u(x) \in L_2(G)$ to have square integrable generalized derivatives of order m if there is a sequence of m- times continuously differentiable functions $u_n(x)$ such that $D^\alpha u_n \to D^\alpha u$ in $L_2(G)$ for all $|\alpha| \leq m$. The totality of such functions $u(x)$ forms a Hilbert space with respect to the inner product

$$(u,v)_{m,2} = \sum_{|\alpha| \leq m} \int_G (D^\alpha u)(D^\alpha v)$$

This space is denoted $W_{m,2}(G)$. The closure of $C_0^\infty(G)$ in $W_{m,2}(G)$ is written $\dot{W}_{m,2}(G)$.

We now give one procedure to reformulate a large class of boundary-value problems associated with partial differential operators in divergence form as abstract operator equations in a Hilbert space $\dot{W}_{m,2}(G)$. (This extends the procedure we have used to prove the results of this section.)

Suppose we are given the nonlinear Dirichlet problem 1"

$$\text{(a)} \quad Au = \sum_{|\alpha| \leq m} D^\alpha(A_\alpha(x,u,\ldots,D^m u)) = 0 \quad \text{in } G$$

$$\text{(b)} \quad D^\alpha u = 0 \quad \text{on } \partial G \quad \text{for } |\alpha| \leq m-1$$

Then we define (i) a <u>classical solution</u> of Problem 1" as a function $u(x)$, $2m$ times continuously differentiable in G and $(m-1)$ times continuously differentiable in $\bar{G}$, satisfying 1" (a) and (b) pointwise,

(ii) a <u>generalized solution</u> of Problem 1" as a function $u(x) \in \dot{W}_{m,2}(G)$ satisfying $a(u,\phi) = 0$ for all $\phi \in \dot{W}_{1,2}(G)$

where $a(u,\phi)$ is the Dirichlet form associated with the operator A.

LEMMA 4-24. *Suppose* $A_\alpha(x,u,\ldots,D^m u) \in L_2(G)$ *for each* $u \in \dot{W}_{m,2}(G)$ *then* $a(u,v) = (\tilde{A}u,v)_{m,2}$ *where* $\tilde{A}$ *is a mapping of* $\dot{W}_{m,2}(G)$ *into itself: and so the generalized solutions of Problem 1" can be obtained by solving the operator equation* $\tilde{A}u = 0$.

Proof. $a(u,v)$ is a functional defined on the Hilbert space $\dot{W}_{m,2}(G)$ and is linear in v. Furthermore by the Cauchy-Schwarz inequality

$$|a(u,v)| \leq \sum_{|\alpha| \leq m} \|A_\alpha\|_{0,2}\|D^\alpha v\|_{0,2} \leq K\|v\|_{m,2}$$

where K is a constant independent of v. Thus by the Riesz Representation Theorem for linear functionals in a Hilbert space, $a(u,v) = (\tilde{A}u,v)_{m,2}$ where $\tilde{A}$ is a mapping of $\dot{W}_{m,2}(G)$ into itself. ||

As before, one can easily show that every classical solution of Problem 1" is a generalized solution. Thus the solvability of Problem 1" can be studied by the methods of Chapter 3.

Exercises

4-11. (i) Prove the equation $y'' = 1 + y'^2$ has no smooth solution satisfying $y(0) = 0$ and $y(\pi) = 0$. (ii) Prove the equation $y'' + \lambda yy' = 0$ has no smooth solution other than $y \equiv 0$ satisfying $y(0) = 0, y(1) = 0$. (iii) Same as (i) for $y'' + e^y = 0$.

4-12. Let G be an arbitrary bounded domain in the plane with boundary ∂G. Suppose n is a positive integer. Prove that the boundary-value problem in G

$$\Delta u - u^{2n+1} = f(x)$$

$$u_{|\partial G} = 0$$

has one and only one generalized solution provided $f(x) \in L_2(G)$. In what sense does the solution depend continuously on f? (Hint: Assume, as known, that the integral $\int_G u^{2n+1}\phi$ defines a bounded linear functional on $\dot{W}_{1,2}(G)$ in ϕ for fixed $u \in \dot{W}_{1,2}(G)$.)

4-13. Let G be an arbitrary bounded domain in $\mathbb{R}^3$. Prove that the boundary-value problem in G

$$\Delta u + u^3 = 0$$

$$u_{|\partial G} = 0$$

always has a solution $u(x) \not\equiv 0$. (Hint: Assume, as known that the integral $\int_G u^3\phi = (Bu,\phi)_{\dot{W}_{1,2}(G)}$ for $u, \phi \in \dot{W}_{1,2}(G)$ where B is a completely continuous mapping of $\dot{W}_{1,2}(G)$ into itself.)

4-14. Let Σ_R denote the sphere of radius R in $\mathbb{R}^3$, that is $\Sigma_R = \{x | x \in \mathbb{R}^3, |x| \leq R\}$. Prove that for sufficiently small R the boundary-value problem in Σ_R

$$\Delta u + u - u^3 = 0$$

$$u_{|\partial \Sigma_R} = 0$$

has the unique solution $u \equiv 0$. Determine the largest number R_c for which this boundary-value problem has a unique solution. Prove the existence of two distinct solutions of this problem for R slightly larger than R_c. (Hint: Same as in Exercise 4-13 above; set $x = Rx'$ where $|x'| = 1$ and apply Theorem 3-23.)

4-15. Let G be a bounded domain in $\mathbb{R}^n$. Prove the boundary-value problem in G

$$\Delta u = g(x,u)$$

$$u|_{\partial G} = 0$$

has a generalized solution in G provided g satisfies the following growth conditions: (i) $g(x,0) \in L_2(G)$, (ii) $|g(x,u) - g(x,v)| \leq K_1 |u-v|$, (iii) $|ug(u)| \leq K_2[1 + |u|]$ where K_1 and K_2 are positive constants. (Hint: Represent the solutions as fixed points of a compact operator T acting in a Hilbert space H, and prove that th degree of the mapping $(I - T)$ is one on sufficiently large spheres in H.)

4-16. Let $\mathfrak{M}$ be a compact two-dimensional manifold with a smooth Riemannian metric $ds^2 = \Sigma_{i,j = 1,2}\, g_{ij} dx_i dx_j$. Suppose with this metric the Gaussian curvature $K(x)$ of $\mathfrak{M}$ satisfies $\int_{\mathfrak{M}} \overline{K}(x) < 0$. Prove that $\overline{\mathfrak{M}}$ is conformall equivalent to a manifold $\overline{\mathfrak{M}}$ with $\overline{K}(x) = \text{const.}$ i.e. there exists a metric $\overline{g}_{ij}$ on $\mathfrak{M}$ with $\overline{g}_{ij} = e^{2\sigma} g_{ij}$, where $\sigma(x$ is a function defined on $\mathfrak{M}$ such that the Gaussian curvature of $\mathfrak{M}$ relative to $\overline{g}_{ij}$ is a constant $\overline{K}$. (Hint:

Assume, as known, that (1) $\int_{\mathcal{M}} e^{2u}\, \phi = (Bu,\phi)$ for $u,\ \phi \in W_{1,2}(\mathcal{M})$ where B is a completely continuous mapping of $W_{1,2}(\mathcal{M})$ into itself, and (2) the function σ can be defined as a solution of the partial differential equation on $\mathcal{M}$

$$2\Delta\sigma - K(x) + \overline{K}e^{2\sigma} = 0$$

where

$$\Delta\sigma = \sum_{i,j} \frac{1}{\sqrt{|g|}} \frac{\partial}{\partial x_i} \left(\sqrt{|g|}\, g^{ij} \frac{\partial\sigma}{\partial x_i}\right)$$

and $|g| = \det(g_{ij})$ and $g_{ij}g^{jk} = \delta_{ik}$. See [6].)

BIBLIOGRAPHY

1. M. Hervé, Several Complex Variables, Oxford Univ. Press, London, 1963.

2. L. Bers, F. John, M. Schechter, Partial Differential Equations, Interscience, New York, 1964.

3. Hardy, Littlewood and Polya, Inequalities, Second Edition, Cambridge Univ. Press, Cambridge, 1959.

4. R. Courant and D. Hilbert, Methods of Mathematical Physics Vol. II, Interscience, New York, 1962.

5. S. Agmon, Lectures on Elliptic Boundary Value Problems, Van Nostrand, Princeton, 1965.

6. L. P. Eisenhart, Riemannian Geometry, Princeton Univ. Press, Princeton, 1927.

APPENDIX I - THE AXIOMS OF HOMOLOGY THEORY

Let $\mathcal{B}$ be the collection of topological spaces. By a homology theory on $\mathcal{B}$, we mean a collection of three functions defined as follows: The first function H assigns to each pair (X,A) in $\mathcal{B}$ and each integer q an Abelian group, $H_q(X,A)$, the q-dimensional homology group. The second function $*$ assigns to each continuous mapping $f\colon (X,A) \to (Y,B) \subset \mathcal{B}$ and to each integer q a group homomorphism $f_*\colon H_q(X,A) \to H_q(Y,B)$, the homomorphism induced by the map f. The third function ∂ assigns to each $(X,A) \subset \mathcal{B}$ and to each integer q a homomorphism $\partial\colon H_q(X,A) \to H_{q-1}(A)$. [Note: $H_{q-1}(A) = H_{q-1}(A,A)$.] These functions are required to satisfy the following seven axioms.

Axiom 1. If i is the identity mapping of $(X,A) \to (X,A)$, then $i_*\colon H_q(X,A) \to H_q(X,A)$ is the identity automorphism for each q.

Axiom 2. If $f\colon (X,A) \to (Y,B)$ and $g\colon (Y,B) \to (Z,C)$, then $(gf)_* = g_* f_*$.

Axiom 3. $\partial f_* = f_* \partial$.

Axiom 4. (Exactness). If $i\colon A \to X$ and $j\colon X \to (X,A)$ denote inclusion maps, then the following infinite sequence is exact, that is, the image of each homomorphism equals the kernel of the next homomorphism

$$\cdots \to H_q(A) \xrightarrow{i_*} H_q(X) \xrightarrow{j_*} H_q(X,A) \xrightarrow{\partial} H_{q-1}(A) \to \cdots$$

Axiom 5. (Homotopy Axiom). If $f, g: (X,A) \to (Y,B)$ are homotopic, then $f_* = g_*$.

Axiom 6. (Excision Axiom). If U is an open subset of X such that $\overline{U} \subset \text{int } A$, the inclusion $e: (X - U, A - U) \to (X,A)$ has induced an isomorphism $e_*: H_q(X - U, A - U) \to H_q(X,A)$.

Axiom 7. (Dimension Axiom). The point 0 has homology groups $H_q(0) = 0$ $(q \neq 0)$.

Let P_0 be a fixed reference point in $\mathcal{B}$, and suppose $H_0(P_0) = G$. Then G is called the coefficient group of the homology theory. Suppose $G = Z$ the additive group of integers, then for the so-called singular homology theory standard computations yield for $\Sigma^n = \{x | x \in \mathbb{R}^n, |x| \leq 1\}$ and $S^{n-1} = \{x | x \in \mathbb{R}^n, |x| = 1\}$:

(a) $H_q(S^n) = \begin{cases} Z & \text{if } q = 0, n \\ 0 & \text{otherwise} \end{cases}$

(b) $H_q(S^0) = \begin{cases} Z + Z & \text{if } q = 0 \\ 0 & \text{otherwise} \end{cases}$

(c) $H_q(\Sigma^n, S^{n-1}) = \begin{cases} Z & \text{if } q = n \\ 0 & \text{otherwise} \end{cases}$

The rank of the Abelian group $H_q(X,A)$ is called the

Betti number $R_q(X,A)$ $(q = 0,1,\ldots,n)$. The sum $\chi(X,A) = \Sigma_{q=0}^{\infty} (-1)^q R_q(X,A)$ is called the Euler-Poincaré characteristic of (X,A). Note that by virtue of axioms (1) - (7), $\chi(X,A)$ satisfies the properties mentioned in Exercises 2-20 and 2-21.

APPENDIX II - STANDARD RESULTS FROM ANALYSIS

Here we gather together those basic facts from analysis which we have mentioned in the course of our study. The reader will find proofs of these results in basic texts in analysis (eg. J. Dieudonné: Foundations of Modern Analysis, and R. C. Buck: Advanced Calculus).

1. _The Implicit Function Theorem_. Let f be a continuously differentiable mapping defined on an open set in $\mathbb{R}^n$ with range in $\mathbb{R}^n$. Suppose $f(x_0) = p$ and the Jacobian determinant of f at x_0, $\det J_f(x_0)$, is nonzero, then f is a local diffeomorphism of a neighborhood of x_0 onto a neighborhood of p.

2. _Tietze Extension Theorem_. Suppose C is a closed subset of a metric space X and $f(x)$ is a continuous bounded real-valued function defined on C. Then $f(x)$ has a continuous real-valued extension $F(x)$ defined on X such that $\sup_X |F(x)| = \sup_C |f(x)|$.

3. _General results for systems of ordinary differential equations of the form_ $dy/dt = f(t,y)$ (_where_ y _and_ f _are vectors in_ $\mathbb{R}^n$).

(i) _Existence_. If $f(t,y)$ is a continuous function of t and y in an open set in $\mathbb{R}^1 \times \mathbb{R}^n$ containing $(0,y_0)$, then the differential equation has a solution $y(t,y_0)$ existing for sufficiently small t which passes through the given point $(0,y_0)$ at $t = 0$.

(ii) Uniqueness and continuous dependence on initial data. If f satisfies a local Lipschitz condition, that is,

$$|f(t,y) - f(t',y')| \leq K_c\{|t - t'| + |y - y'|\}$$

for $|y - y_0|$, $|t| \leq c$, where K_c is a constant depending only on c, then the differential equation has a unique solution passing through the point $(0,y_0)$. If we denote this solution by $y(t,y_0)$, then $y(t,y_0)$ depends continuously on y_0 provided $|y - y_0|$ and $|t|$ are sufficiently small.

4. Contraction Mapping Principle. For complete metric spaces X with metric $d(,)$, suppose A is a mapping of X into itself which satisfies the inequality

$$d(Ax,Ay) \leq Kd(x,y)$$

for every $x,y \in X$, where K is a constant strictly less than 1 and independent of x and y. Then the equation $Ax = x$ has one and only one solution in X.

5. Some facts concerning Hilbert spaces H. A linear functional $\mathcal{L}(x)$ defined on H is bounded if $|\mathcal{L}(x)| \leq K\|x\|$

where K is a constant independent of x. Bounded linear functionals in H are continuous with respect to strong convergence. Furthermore we note

(i) Riesz Representation Theorem for bounded linear functionals defined on H. Let $\mathcal{L}(x)$ be a bounded linear functional defined on H, then $\mathcal{L}(x) = (z,x)$ for some unique fixed $z \in H$, where $(\, , \,)$ denotes the inner product defined on H.

(ii) Schwarz inequality. $|(z,x)| \leq \|z\| \|x\|$. Consequently, $\|x\| = \sup_{\|v\|=1} (x,v)$.

(iii) Orthogonal complement and projection operator. Every closed subspace L of H is also a Hilbert space, and every vector x in H can be uniquely represented in the form $x = x' + x''$ where $x' \in L$ and $x'' \in H - L$. x' is called the projection of x on L. $H - L$ is called the orthogonal complement of L in H (denoted $L^{\perp}$), and is itself a closed linear subspace of H. The linear mapping P, defined on H by setting $Px = x'$, is called the projection operator (or projector) of H onto L. P is a self-adjoint bounded mapping and $P^2 = P$.

(iv) Bounded operators. A linear operator A mapping a Banach space B into itself is bounded if $\|Ax\| = K\|x\|$ holds for all $x \in B$ where K is a constant independent of x. The smallest such K is called the norm of A, and denoted $\|A\|$. Such a bounded operator A is continuous with respect to strong convergence in B. A has a bounded inverse in B if and only if the range of A is dense in B and for all $x \in B$, $\|Ax\| \geq K_1\|x\|$ where K_1 is a constant independent of $x \in B$. In particular, if L is a compact operator mapping a Hilbert space H into itself and the equation $(I - L)x = 0$ has no solutions not identically zero, then the operator $A = I - L$ has a bounded inverse in H. More generally, if the operator A is not necessarily linear, A is said to be bounded if it maps bounded sets into bounded sets; note that a bounded nonlinear mapping need not be continuous with respect to convergence in norm.